A Note to Students:

Welcome to a new year of math! In this course, you will learn to use new models and methods to think about problems as well as solve them. You will be developing powerful mathematical tools and learning new ways of thinking about and investigating situations. You will be making connections, discovering relationships, figuring out what strategies can be used to solve problems, and explaining your thinking. Learning to think in these ways and communicate about your thinking is useful in mathematical contexts, other subjects in school, and situations outside the classroom. The mathematics you have learned in the past will be valuable for learning in this course. That work, and what you learn in this course, will prepare you for future courses.

In meeting the challenges of this course, you will not be learning alone. You will cooperate with other students as a member of a study team. Being a part of a team means speaking up and interacting with other people. You will explain your ideas, listen to what others have to say, and ask questions if there is something you do not understand. In this course, a single problem can often be solved several ways. You will see problems in different ways than your teammates do. Each of you has something to contribute while you work on the lessons in this course.

Together, your team will complete problems and activities that will help you discover mathematical ideas and develop solution methods. Your teacher will support you as you work, but will not take away your opportunity to think and investigate for yourself. Each topic will be revisited many times and will connect to other topics. If something is not clear to you the first time you work on it, you will have more chances to build your understanding as the course continues.

Learning math this way has an advantage: as long as you actively participate, make sure everyone in your study team is involved, and ask good questions, you will find yourself understanding mathematics at a deeper level than ever before. By the end of this course, you will have a powerful set of mathematical tools to use to solve new problems. With your teammates you will meet mathematical challenges you would not have known how to approach before.

In addition to the support provided by your teacher and your study team, CPM has also created online resources to help you, including help with homework, and a parent guide with extra practice. You will find these resources and more at www.cpm.org.

We wish you well and are confident that you will enjoy this next year of learning!

Sincerely,

The CPM Team

Core Connections, Course 2
Second Edition*, Version 5.0, Volume 2

Managing Editors / Authors

Leslie Dietiker, Ph.D., Director of Curriculum (Both Editions)
Boston University
Boston, MA

Evra Baldinger (First Edition)
University of California, Berkeley
Berkeley, CA

Michael Kassarjian (2nd Edition)
CPM Educational Program
Kensington, CA

Barbara Shreve (First Edition)
San Lorenzo High School
San Lorenzo, CA

Misty Nikula (2nd Edition)
CPM Educational Program
Bellingham, WA

Contributing Authors

Elizabeth Baker
Zane Middle School

Tara Bianchi
American Canyon Middle School

Bev Brockhoff
Glen Edwards Middle School

Clanci Chiu
Santa Barbara Junior High School

Mark Coté
Beaver Lake Middle School

Suzanne Cisco Cox
Turner Middle School

Kathleen Davies
Rincon Valley Middle School

Josea Eggink
Bloomington Public Schools

William Funkhouser
Zane Middle School

Lori Hamada
CPM Educational Program

Brian Hoey
CPM Educational Program

Janet Hollister
La Cumbre Jr. High School

Carol Jancsi
CPM Mentor Teacher

Rakesh Khanna
Hotmath, Inc.

Judy Kysh, Ph.D.
San Francisco State University

Sarah Maile
CPM Educational Program

Bruce Melhorn
International School Bangkok (ISB)

Chris Mikles
Post Falls Middle School

Bob Petersen
CPM Educational Program

Tom Sallee, Ph.D.
University of California, Davis

Lorna Thomas Vázquez
Neillsville, WI Math Consultant

Stephanie Whitney, Ph.D.
DePaul University

Program Directors

Elizabeth Coyner
Christian Brothers High School
Sacramento, CA

Leslie Dietiker, Ph.D.
Boston University
Boston, MA

Lori Hamada
CPM Educational Program
Fresno, CA

Brian Hoey
CPM Educational Program
Sacramento, CA

Michael Kassarjian
CPM Educational Program
Kensington, CA

Judy Kysh, Ph.D.
Departments of Education and
Mathematics San Francisco
State University, CA

Tom Sallee, Ph.D.
Department of Mathematics
University of California, Davis

Karen Wootton
CPM Educational Program
Odenton, MD

*Based on *Making Connections*: *Foundations for Algebra, Courses 1 and 2.*

e-book Manager
Carol Cho
Director of Technology
Martinez, CA

e-book Programmers
Rakesh Khanna
Daniel Kleinsinger
Kevin Stein

e-book Assistants
Debbie Dodd
Shirley Paulsen
Wendy Papciak
Anna Poehlmann
Jordan Wight

Assessment Manager
Karen Wootton
Director of Assessment
Odenton, MD

Assessment Assistants
Elizabeth Baker
Zane Middle School
Eureka, CA

William Funkhouser
Zane Middle School
Eureka, CA

Assessment Website
Elizabeth Fong
Michael Huang
Daniel Kleinsinger

Illustration
Kevin Coffey
San Francisco, CA

Jonathan Weast
Sacramento, CA

Homework Help Manager
Bob Petersen
CPM Educational Program

Homework Help Website
Carol Cho
Director of Technology

Parent Guide with Extra Practice
Elizabeth Coyner
Christian Brothers High School

Brian Hoey
CPM Educational Program

Bob Petersen
CPM Educational Program

Based on the Skill Builder materials created for Foundations for Algebra (2003), created by:

Heidi Ackley	Steve Ackley	Elizabeth Baker
Bev Brockhoff	Ellen Cafferata	Elizabeth Coyner
Scott Coyner	Sara Effenbeck	William Funkhouser
Brian Hoey	Judy Kysh	Kris Petersen
Robert Petersen	Edwin Reed	Stacy Rocklein
Kristie Sallee	Tom Sallee	Howard Webb

Technical Managers
Sarah Maile   Aubrie Maze

Technical Assistants

Stephanie Achondo	Robert Ainsworth	Bethany Armstrong
Rebecca Bobell	Delenn Breedlove	Jason Cho
Hannah Coyner	Mary Coyner	Carmen de la Cruz
Matthew Donahue	Bethany Firch	Dana Kimball
Leslie Lai	Michael Li	Jerry Luo
Eli Marable	James McCardle	Nyssa Muheim
Alexandra Murphy	Wendy Papciak	Atlanta Parrott
Ryan Peabody	Iris Perez	Steven Pham
Anna Poehlmann	Eduardo Ramirez	John Ramos
Ali Rivera	Andrea Smith	Rachel Smith
Claire Taylor	Christy Van Beek	Megan Walters
Sarah Wong	Alex Yu	

4 5 6 7 8 9   20 19 18 17 16   Version 5.0

Printed in the United States of America   ISBN: 978-1-60328-083-9

Core Connections, Course 2
Student Edition

Volume 1

Volume 2

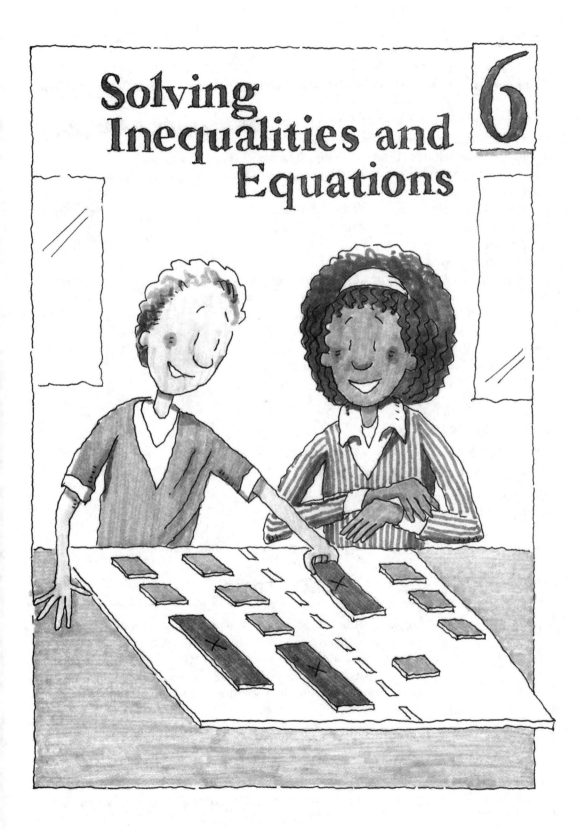

Solving Inequalities and Equations

6

CHAPTER 6   Solving Inequalities and Equations

In this chapter you will use algebra tiles to compare two expressions on Expression Comparison Mats. In Section 6.1, you will also discover the legal moves that allow you to simplify expressions. Then you will determine which expression is greater or if they are equal. You will also learn how to record solutions to inequalities using number lines with boundary points.

You will extend what you know about comparing expressions to include cases in which expressions are equal. You will build equations on Equation Mats with algebra tiles, write equations with variables, and solve equations without using tiles. Learning how to write and solve equations will provide you a new way to solve word problems without completing a 5-D table. By the end of this chapter, you will learn efficient ways to justify the steps used to solve equations.

Guiding Questions

Think about these questions throughout this chapter:

What's the relationship?

Are they equivalent?

How can I represent it?

How can I solve it?

In this chapter, you will learn how to:

➤ Simplify and compare two algebraic expressions.

➤ Write and solve algebraic inequalities.

➤ Solve for a variable when two expressions are equal.

➤ Write and solve an equation to solve a word problem.

➤ Recognize when an equation has no solution or infinite solutions.

Chapter Outline

Section 6.1 In the first section, you will learn additional strategies for comparing expressions. The strategies will involve maintaining equivalence and determining relationships between expressions. You will also solve inequalities and represent their solutions on a number line.

Section 6.2 Using algebra tiles, here you will explore what you can learn when expressions are equal. Solving equations will also provide you an opportunity to develop efficient simplification strategies and to learn how to know that your solution is correct. You will also consider special cases, such as when an equation has no solution.

6.1.1 How do these compare?

Comparing Expressions

In Chapter 4, you worked with writing and simplifying expressions. As you wrote expressions, you learned that it was helpful to simplify them by combining like terms and removing zeros. In this lesson, you and your teammates will use a tool for comparing expressions. The tool will allow you to determine whether one expression is greater than the other or if they are equivalent ways of writing the same thing (that is, if they are equal).

Remember that to represent expressions with algebra tiles, you will need to be very careful about how positives and negatives are distinguished. To help you understand the diagrams in the text, the legend at right will be placed on every page containing a mat. It shows the shading for +1 and –1. This model also represents a zero pair.

6-1. **COMPARING EXPRESSIONS**

Ignacio and Oliver were playing a game. Each of them grabbed a handful of algebra tiles. They wanted to see whose expression had the greater value.

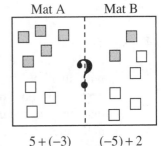

Mat A   Mat B

$5 + (-3)$ $(-5) + 2$

Two expressions can be compared by dividing the expression mat in half to change it into an **Expression Comparison Mat**. Then the two expressions can be built side by side and compared to see which one is greater.

- Oliver put his tiles on Mat A in the picture above and described it as $5 + (-3)$.

- Ignacio put his tiles on Mat B and said it was $(-5) + 2$.

With your team, find two different methods to simplify the two expressions so you can compare them. Which side of the mat is larger?

6-2. Using your Expression Comparison Mat, build the two expressions at right. Find a way to determine which side is greater, if possible. Show your work by sketching it on the Lesson 6.1.1B Resource Page. Be ready to share your conclusion and your justification.

Mat A   Mat B

6-3.   MORE COMPARING EXPRESSIONS – Is one expression greater?

Consider how you were able to compare the expressions in the previous
problems. When is it possible to remove tiles to compare the expressions on the
mats? In this problem, you will work with your team to identify two different
"legal moves" for simplifying expressions.

Build the mat below using tiles and simplify the expressions. Record your work
by drawing circles around the zeros or the balanced sets of tiles that you remove
in each step on the Lesson 6.1.1B Resource Page. Which expression is greater?

6-4.   There are two kinds of moves you could
use in problem 6-3 to simplify expressions
with algebra tiles. First, you could remove
zeros. Second, you could remove
matching (or balanced) sets of tiles from
both sides of the mat. Both moves are
shown in the figures below. Justify why
each of these moves can be used to
simplify expressions.

Removing Balanced Sets   **Removing Zeros**

6-5. WHICH SIDE IS GREATER?

For each of the problems below, use the Lesson 6.1.1 Resource Page and:

- Build the two expressions on your mat.

- Write an expression for each side below the mats for parts (a) through (d) OR draw the tiles in the space given on the resource page for parts (e) and (f).

- Use legal moves to determine which mat is greater, if possible. Record your work by drawing circles around the zeros or the balanced (matching) sets of tiles that you remove in each problem.

a.

b.

c.

d.

e. Mat A: $3x - 4 - 2$

Mat B: $3(x - 1)$

f. Mat A: $5 + (-3x) + 5x$

Mat B: $x^2 + 2x + 1 - x^2$

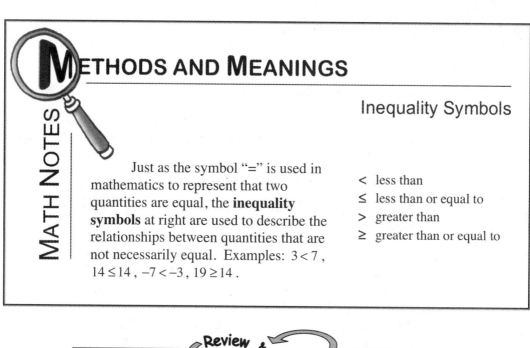

METHODS AND MEANINGS

Inequality Symbols

Just as the symbol "=" is used in mathematics to represent that two quantities are equal, the **inequality symbols** at right are used to describe the relationships between quantities that are not necessarily equal. Examples: $3 < 7$, $14 \leq 14$, $-7 < -3$, $19 \geq 14$.

$<$ less than
$\leq$ less than or equal to
$>$ greater than
$\geq$ greater than or equal to

Review & Preview

6-6.   Write the expression shown on each of the Expression Mats below. Then simplify them by making zeros and combining like terms.   ■ = +1   □ = −1

a.

b.

6-7.   Which expressions are equivalent to the perimeter of the shape? How do you know?

a. $x + 3 + 3x + 1$ b. $2x + 4 + x$

c. $4x + 4$ d. $2x + 2 + 2x + 2$

Core Connections, Course 2

6-8.   Simplify the following expressions.

a. $-\frac{3}{4}-\frac{2}{5}$

b. $\frac{7}{8}-\frac{2}{3}$

c. $\frac{1}{3}-\frac{5}{6}$

d. $1\frac{2}{3}+(-\frac{2}{5})$

e. $\frac{4}{7}-(-\frac{3}{8})$

f. $-4\frac{1}{2}+3\frac{1}{9}$

6-9.   Desmond is rolling a standard six-sided number cube. He plans to roll it 72 times.

a.   About how many times would you expect Desmond to roll a 4? Why?

b.   About how many times would you expect him to roll an even number? Why?

c.   Desmond kept track of his results for all 72 rolls. The table at right shows some of his results.

Based on his partial results, how many times did he roll a 5 or a 6?

Result	Number of Outcomes
1	9
2	14
3	11
4	8

6-10.   In parts (a) through (c) below, you will see pairs of quantities. For each pair of quantities, use words to write a sentence that describes the relationship. For example, "$5, $8" could be, "$8 is three more than $5."

a. $13, $39

b.   25 feet, 17 feet

c.   38 lbs., 19 lbs.

6-11.   Copy each part below on your paper. Then use the number line to help you fill in < (less than) or > (greater than) on the blank line.

$$-15\ -10\ -5\ \ 0\ \ 5\ \ 10\ \ 15$$

a. -5 ___ -2

b. 8 ___ -1

c. -5 ___ 0

d. -15 ___ -14

6.1.2 What if I cannot tell?

Comparing Quantities with Variables

Have you ever tried to make a decision when the information you have is uncertain? Perhaps you have tried to make plans on a summer day only to learn that it *might* rain. In that case, your decision might have been based on the weather, such as, "I will go swimming if it does not rain, or stay home and play video games if it does rain." Sometimes in mathematics, solutions might depend on something you do not know, like the value of the variable. Today you will study this kind of situation.

6-12. For each of the problems below, build the given expressions on your Expression Comparison Mat. Then use the simplification strategies of removing zeros and simplifying by removing matching pairs of tiles to determine which side is greater, if possible. Record your steps on the Lesson 6.1.2 Resource Page.

■ = +1
□ = −1

a.

b. Mat A: $2(x+3)-4$

Mat B: $3x+(-1)-x+4$

c.

d.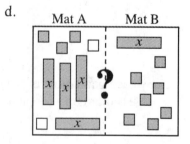

6-13.   WHAT HAPPENED?

When Ignacio and Oliver compared the expressions in part (d) of
problem 6-12, they could not figure out which side was greater.

a.   Is it always possible to determine which
     side of the Expression Comparison Mat is
     greater (has the greater value)? Why or
     why not? Be prepared to share your
     reasoning.

b.   How is it possible for Mat A to have the
     greater value?

c.   How is it possible for Mat B to have the
     greater value?

d.   In what other way can Mat A and B be related? Explain.

6-14.   Ignacio and Oliver are playing another game with
         the algebra tiles. After they simplify two new
         expressions, they are left with the expressions on
         their mats shown at right. They could not tell
         which part of the mat is greater just by looking.

a.   One way to compare the mats is to separate
     the x-tiles and the unit tiles on different sides
     of the mat. Work with your team to find a
     way to have only x-tiles on Mat A. Make sure
     that you are able to justify that your moves are
     legal.

b.   Using the same reasoning from part (a), what
     would you do to have only the variable on
     Mat B in the Expression Comparison Mat at
     right?

c.   Write a short note to Ignacio and Oliver
     explaining this new strategy. Feel free to
     give it a name so it is easier for them to
     remember.

6-15.   Ignacio and Oliver are trying to decide if there are other ways
to change expressions on the Expression Comparison Mat
without affecting which side is greater. They have invented
some new strategies and described them below.

Your Task: For each of the moves below:

- Build the Expression Comparison Mats on your paper.

- Follow each set of directions for the mat shown in each
strategy below.

- Determine if the move in the strategy is valid for maintaining the
relationship between the two expressions. Be prepared to justify your
response.

Strategy #1

*"If you have a mat like the one
drawn below, you can add the
same number of tiles to both sides.
In this case, I added 3 negative
tiles to both sides."*

Strategy #2

*"On a mat like the one below, I added
+3 to Mat A and added –3 to Mat B."*

Strategy #3

*"To simplify, I removed a positive
x-tile from one side and a negative
x-tile from the other side."*

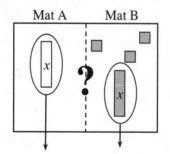

Strategy #4

*"On a mat like the one below, I would
add three zero pairs to Mat B."*

6-16.   LEARNING LOG

In your Learning Log, summarize the methods that
your team and class developed in the last two lessons to
simplify expressions on the Expression Comparison
Mat. Label your Learning Log entry "Simplifying
Expressions (Legal Moves)" and include today's date.

6-17.   Write an algebraic expression for each mat below. Then use the legal
moves that you have developed to simplify each mat. If possible,
decide which expression is greater.

☐ = +1
☐ = –1

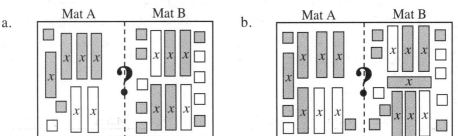

a.   Mat A   Mat B

b.   Mat A   Mat B

6-18.   When solving a problem about the perimeter of a rectangle using the 5-D
Process, Herman built the expression below.

$$\text{Perimeter} = x + x + 4x + 4x \text{ feet}$$

a.   Draw a rectangle and label its sides based on Herman's expression.

b.   What is the relationship between the base and height of Herman's
rectangle? How can you tell?

c.   If the perimeter of the rectangle is 60 feet, how long are the base and height
of Herman's rectangle? Show how you know.

6-19.   Evaluate the expressions below.

a. $5^2 \cdot (-3) - 4 \cdot 6 + 7$

b. $-3 \cdot (6 + 4 \cdot 2)$

c. $9 + 8 \div (-4) - 12$

d. $2^3 - 3 \cdot 4 + 6(-1 + 2)$

e. $4 + (3 + 4)^2$

f. $\frac{8-13}{10}$

6-20.   Write each of the following expressions in two ways, one with parentheses and one without. For example, $4(x-3)$ can be written $4x-12$.

   a.   A number reduced by 3 and then multiplied by 2.

   b.   A number increased by 7 and then multiplied by 5.

   c.   Ten times a number, and then add twenty.

6-21.   Graph these points on a coordinate grid: $A(-2,0)$, $B(0,4)$, $C(4,1)$, $D(2,-3)$. Connect the points in order, with point D connected to point A. What shape have you created?

6-22.   Alan was paying a dinner check, but he was not sure how much he should tip for his bill of $27.38. If a 15% tip is standard, about how much should Alan leave for the server?

6.1.3   Where do the solutions begin and end?

One Variable Inequalities

You have used Expression Comparison Mats to compare two expressions and have found that sometimes it is possible to determine which expression is greater. In this lesson, you will again compare expressions. This time, you will find the values for the variable that make one expression greater than the other.

■ = +1
□ = −1

6-23.   Maria has been recording her work to see which side of an Expression Comparison Mat is greater, but she has been called away. Garth looked at her work, but he cannot figure out what Maria did to get from one step to another.

Mat A	Mat B
$5x + 2 + (-6)$	$2x + 2 + (-8)$
$5x + (-4)$	$2x + (-6)$
$3x + (-4)$	-6
$3x$	-2

Look at Maria's work above and help Garth by building the expressions on your mat and simplifying them. Write him a note explaining what Maria did to get from one step to another.

Core Connections, Course 2

6-24.   Compare the expressions 2 + 2x + (–3) on Mat A and 2x + (–4) + 1 on Mat B using algebra tiles. Use Maria's method of recording to show your steps. Make sure you record each step so that your teacher or others could see what you did on your Expression Comparison Mat.

   a.   Which mat is greater?

   b.   Use symbols such as <, =, or > to show the relationship between the final expressions on Mat A and Mat B.

6-25.   Maria and Garth were playing a game with the algebra tiles. They each grabbed a handful of tiles and put them on the Expression Comparison Mat at right to see whose side had greater value.

Maria said, *"I have Mat A and my side has more value."* Garth, who had Mat B, disagreed with her.

   a.   Write expressions for Mat A and Mat B.

   b.   Work with your team to simplify the expressions on the Expression Comparison Mat while carefully recording your work for each step on your paper with symbols. Can you tell whose side is greater? Why or why not?

   c.   With your team, find at least four values for x that would make the expression on Maria's side (Mat A) greater than the expression on Garth's side (Mat B). Be prepared to share your values with the class.

   d.   Any value for x that makes Mat A greater than Mat B is a solution to the inequality $2x+3+(-1)>x+5$. This is read, *"Two x plus three plus negative one is greater than x plus five."*

   Share your solutions with another team and see if you have the same solutions as the other team does.

6-26. Karla had a hard time keeping track of all of the solutions to the inequality in problem 6-25 in her head. She decided to try to organize her answers. First she needed to know more about the problem.

a. Is there a greatest number that is a solution? Discuss this question with your team and be prepared to share your ideas with the class.

b. Is there a smallest number that is a solution? Again, be prepared to share your team's thinking with the class.

c. What is special about the point where the solutions end? (This number is called the **boundary point**.) In other words, what relationship does this number have to the two expressions being compared?

d. Karla was tired of listing so many solutions and wanted a quick way to show all of the solutions to this inequality. She decided to draw a number line like the one below.

On your own paper, draw a number line such as the one above then follow your teacher's directions to represent the answer to this question on your number line.

6-27. Now consider the inequality $2x + 5 < 3$, which can be read "*Two x plus five is less than 3.*"

$\blacksquare = +1$
$\square = -1$

Build the inequality on your Expression Comparison Mat and record each step on your paper using symbols. Work with your team to describe the least and greatest solutions to the inequality and draw your solution on a number line. Be prepared to justify your ideas.

6-28. Jerry and Ken were solving the inequality $6 > 2x + 2$. They set up the inequality on their Expression Comparison Mat and simplified it.

a. Write a sentence in words to represent the original inequality.

b. What did they get on each side of the mat when they simplified? Record your work on your paper.

c. Graph all the solutions to this inequality on a number line.

Ⓜ️ETHODS AND MEANINGS

Algebra Vocabulary

Variable: A letter or symbol that represents one or more numbers.

Expression: A combination of numbers, variables, and operation symbols. An expression does not contain an equal sign. For example, $2x + 3(5 - 2x) + 8$. Also, $5 - 2x$ is a smaller expression within the larger expression.

Term: Parts of the expression separated by addition and subtraction. For example, in the expression $2x + 3(5 - 2x) + 8$, the three terms are $2x$, $3(5 - 2x)$, and 8. The expression $5 - 2x$ has two terms, 5 and $2x$.

Coefficient: The numerical part of a term. In the expression $2x + 3(5 - 2x) + 8$, 2 is the coefficient of $2x$. In the expression $7x - 15x^2$, both 7 and 15 are coefficients.

Constant term: A number that is not multiplied by a variable. In the example above, 8 is a constant term. The number 3 is not a constant term because it is multiplied by a variable inside the parentheses.

Factor: Part of a multiplication expression. In the expression $3(5 - 2x)$, 3 and $5 - 2x$ are factors.

Review & Preview

6-29.   Graph each of the following inequalities on a number line.

a. $x > 3$ b. $x \le 5$ c. $x \ge -4$

6-30.   Write an algebraic expression for each situation. For example, 5 less than a number can be expressed as $n - 5$.

a.   7 more than a number   b.   Twice a number

6-31.   MATH TALK

Read the Math Notes box in this lesson to review commonly used algebra
vocabulary. Then consider the expression below as you answer the following
questions.
$$3x^2 + 7 - 2(4x+1)$$

a.   Name the constant term.

b.   What are the two factors in $2(4x+1)$? What are the two factors in $4x$?

c.   Write an expression with a variable m, a coefficient -3, and a constant of
17.

d.   Use the words coefficient, constant term, term, expression, and variable, to
discuss $4x^2 + 11y - 37$.

e.   Use the words factor, product, quotient, and sum to describe the parts of
$\frac{5-m}{n} - 2 - 8(m+n)$.

6-32.   Hector has a part-time job at a garage. He gets a paycheck of $820 every four
weeks.

a.   Hector has to pay 15% of his income in taxes. How much money does he
pay in taxes each paycheck? Show your thinking with a diagram and
calculations.

b.   Hector took a 1-week vacation, so his next paycheck will only be for 3
weeks of work. What percentage of his regular pay should he expect to
receive? How much is that?

c.   The garage owner is impressed with Hector's work and is giving him a
10% raise. How much will Hector be paid when he receives his next 4-
week paycheck?

6-33.   A fair number cube labeled 1, 2, 3, 4, 5, and 6 is rolled 100 times. About how
many times would you expect the number 3 to appear?

6-34.   Find the perimeter and area of each algebra tile shape below. Be sure to
combine like terms.

a.   b.

6.1.4 How can I find all solutions?

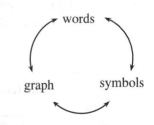

Solving One Variable Inequalities

In this lesson, you will work with your team to develop and describe a process for solving linear inequalities. As you work, use the following questions to focus your discussion.

What is a solution?

What do all of the solutions have in common?

What is the greatest solution? What is the smallest solution?

6-35. Jerry and Ken were working on solving the inequality $3x - 1 \le 2x$. They found the boundary point and Ken made the number line graph shown at right.

Jerry noticed a problem. *"Doesn't the line at the bottom of the $\le$ symbol mean that it includes the equal part? That means that $x = 1$ is also a solution. How could we show that?"*

"Hmmm," Jerry said. *"Well, the solution $x = 1$ would look like this on a number line. Is there a way that we can combine the two number lines?"*

Discuss this idea with your team and be prepared to share your ideas with the class.

6-36. The diagram at right shows three possible ways to represent inequality statements. Review the meanings of the inequality symbols >, <, ≥, and ≤ with your team. Then, generate the two missing representations from each inequality described in parts (a) through (c) below.

a. $x < -1\frac{1}{2}$

b. x is greater than or equal to two.

c.

6-37.   WHEN IS THE BOUNDARY POINT INCLUDED?

Represent the solution for each of the variables described below as an inequality on a number line and with symbols.

a. The speed limit on certain freeways is 65 miles per hour. Let x represent any speed that could get a speeding ticket.

b. You brought $10 to the mall. Let y represent any amount of money you can spend.

c. To ride your favorite roller coaster, you must be at least five feet tall but less than seven feet tall. Let h represent any height that can ride the roller coaster.

6-38.   Ellie was still working on her dollhouse. She has boards that are two different lengths. One long board is 54 inches.

a. The length of the short board is unknown. Ellie put three short boards end-to-end and then added her 12-inch ruler end-to-end. The total length was still less than the 54-inch board. Draw a picture showing how the short and long boards are related.

b. Write an inequality that represents the relationship between the short boards and 54 inches shown in your diagram in part (a). Be sure to state what your variable represents.

c. What are possible lengths of the short board? Show your answer as an inequality and on a number line.

6-39. Jordyn, Teri, and Morgan are going to have a kite-flying contest. Jordyn and Teri each have one roll of kite string. They also each have 45 yards of extra string. Morgan has three rolls of kite string plus 10 yards of extra string. All of the rolls of string are the same length. The girls want to see who can fly their kite the highest.

a. Since Jordyn and Teri have fewer rolls of kite string, they decide to tie their string together so their kite can fly higher. Write at least two expressions to show how much kite string Jordyn and Teri have. Let x represent the number of yards of string on one roll.

b. Write an expression to show how much kite string Morgan has. Again, let x be the number of yards of string on one roll.

c. How long does a roll of string have to be for Jordyn and Teri to be able to fly their kite higher than Morgan's kite? Show your answer as an inequality and on a number line.

d. How long does a roll of string have to be for Morgan to be able to fly her kite higher than Jordyn and Teri's kite? Show your answer as an inequality and on a number line.

e. What length would the roll of string have to be for the girls' kites to fly at the same height?

6-40. **Additional Challenge:** Travis loves trains! Today he is beginning a train ride from Madison, Wisconsin all the way to Seattle, Washington.

Shortly after the train left the station in Madison, Travis fell asleep. When he woke up, it was dark outside and he had no idea how long he had been asleep. A fellow passenger told him they had already passed La Crosse, which is 135 miles from Madison. If the train travels at an average speed of 50 miles per hour, at least how long has Travis been asleep? Represent this problem with an inequality and then solve it.

6-41. LEARNING LOG

Work with your team to describe each step of your process for finding boundary points and deciding what part of the number line to shade. Then write down each step in your Learning Log. Be sure to illustrate your ideas with examples. Title this entry "Finding Boundary Points" and label it with today's date.

METHODS AND MEANINGS

Graphing Inequalities

To solve and graph an inequality with one variable, first treat the problem as if it were an equality and solve the problem. The solution to the equality is called the **boundary point**. For example, to solve $x - 4 \geq 8$, first solve $x - 4 = 8$. The solution $x = 12$ is the boundary point for the inequality $x - 4 \geq 8$.

Since the original inequality is true when $x = 12$, place your boundary point on the number line as a solid point. Then test one value on either side in the *original* inequality by substituting it into the original inequality. This will determine which set of numbers makes the inequality true. Write the inequality solution and extend an arrow onto the number line in the direction of the side that makes the inequality true. This is shown with the examples of $x = 8$ and $x = 15$ above. Therefore, the solution is $x \geq 12$ (also shown on the number line).

Test: $x = 8$	Test: $x = 15$
$(8) - 4 \geq 8$	$(15) - 4 \geq 8$
$4 \geq 8$	$11 \geq 8$
FALSE!	TRUE!

When the inequality is $<$ or $>$, the boundary point is *not* included in the answer. On a number line, this would be indicated with an open circle at the boundary point. For example, the graph of $x < 7$ is shown below.

Review & Preview

6-42.   Solve each of the following inequalities. Represent the solutions algebraically (with symbols) and graphically (on a number line).

a. $3x - 3 < 2 - 2x$

b. $\frac{4}{5} x \geq 8$

6-43.   Determine whether each of the numbers below is a solution to the inequality $3x - 2 < 2 - 2x$. Show all of your work.

a.   2

b. $\frac{1}{2}$

c. -3

d. $\frac{2}{3}$

6-44.   Evaluate the expressions below using $x = -2$, $y = -5$, and $z = 3$.

   a. xyz b. $3(x+y)$ c. $\frac{z+2}{y} + 1$

6-45.   On your paper, sketch the algebra tile shape at right. Write an expression for the perimeter, and then find the perimeter for each of the given values of x.

   a. $x = 7$ cm   b. $x = 5.5$ cm

6-46.   Alden found a partially completed 5-D table:

	Define		Do	Decide
				Target 74
Trial 1: 15	$2(15) = 30$	$15 + 2 = 17$	$15 + 30 + 17 =$	62 too small
Trial 2: 18	$2(18) = 36$	$18 + 2 = 20$	$18 + 36 + 20 =$	74 just right

   a.   Create a word problem that could have been solved using this table.

   b.   What words would you put above the numbers in the three empty sections in the "Trial" and "Define" parts of the table?

   c.   What word(s) would you put above the "Do" column?

6-47.   Beth is filling a small backyard pool with a garden hose. The pool holds 30 gallons of water. After 5 minutes, the pool is about one fourth full.

   a.   Assuming that the water is flowing at a constant rate, about how much water is going into the pool each minute?

   b.   About how long will it take to fill the pool?

6.2.1 What values make expressions equal?

Solving Equations

In the last section, you figured out how to determine what values of x make one expression greater than another. In this lesson, you will study what can be learned about x when two expressions are equal. As you work today, focus on these questions:

What if both sides are equal?

Is there more than one way to simplify?

What value(s) of x will make the expressions equal?

6-48.   CHOOSING A PRICE PLAN

Sandeep works at a bowling alley that currently charges players $3 to rent shoes and $4 per game. However, his boss is thinking about charging $11 to rent shoes and $2 per game.

a.   If a customer rents shoes and plays two games, will he or she pay more with the current price plan or the new price plan? Show how you know.

b.   If the customer bowls 7 games, which price plan is cheaper?

6-49.   WILL THEY EVER BE EQUAL?

Sandeep decided to represent the two price plans from problem 6-48 with the expressions below, where x represents the number of games bowled. Then he placed them on the Expression Comparison Mat shown at right.

Original price: $4x+3$ New price: $2x+11$

a.   Are his expressions correct? Find both the original and new prices when $x=2$ and then again when $x=7$ games. Did you get the same prices as you found in problem 6-46?

Problem continues on next page. →

6-49.   *Problem continued from previous page.*

b.   Sandeep then simplified the expressions on the mat. What steps did Sandeep take to simplify the mat to this point?

c.   Sandeep noticed that for a certain number of games, customers would pay the same amount no matter which price plan his boss used. That is, he found a value of x that will make $4x+3=2x+11$. How many games would that customer bowl? What was the price he paid? Explain.

d.   The value of x you found in part (c) is called a **solution** to the equation $4x+3=2x+11$ because it makes the equation true. That is, it makes both expressions have the same value.

Is $x=6$ also a solution? How can you tell?

6-50.   SOLVING FOR X

When the expressions on each side of the comparison mat are equal, they can be represented on a mat called an **Equation Mat**. Obtain a Lesson 6.2.1 Resource Page and algebra tiles from your teacher. Now the "=" symbol on the central line indicates that the expressions on each side of the mat are equal.

a.   Build the equation represented by the Equation Mat at right on your own mat using algebra tiles.

b.   On your paper, record the original equation represented on your Equation Mat.

c.   Simplify the tiles on the mat as much as possible. Record what is on the mat after each legal move as you simplify each expression. What value of x will make the expressions equal?

6-51.   Amelia wants to solve the equation shown on the Equation Mat at right. After she simplified each expression as much as possible, she was confused by the tiles that were left on the mat.

a.   What was Amelia's original equation?

b.   Remove any zero pairs that you find on each side of the Equation Mat. What happens?

c.   What is the solution to this equation? That is, what value of x makes this equation true? Explain your reasoning.

6-52.   Amelia now wants to solve the equation $2x + 2 + (-3) = 5x + 8$. Help her find the value of x that makes these expressions equal. Be sure to:

- Build the expressions using algebra tiles on your Equation Mat.
- Draw the mat on your paper.
- Simplify the mat to help you figure out what value of x makes this equation true. Be sure to record your work in symbols on your paper.

6-53.   **Additional Challenge:** Try the number puzzle below.

Pick any number, add 20, multiply your answer by 2, and subtract 30 from the result. Then, divide your answer by 2 and subtract your original number.

a.   What is the result?

b.   Try it with several different numbers. Is the result the same every time?

c.   Using a variable (such as n) to represent the starting number, show why the final result is always the number 5.

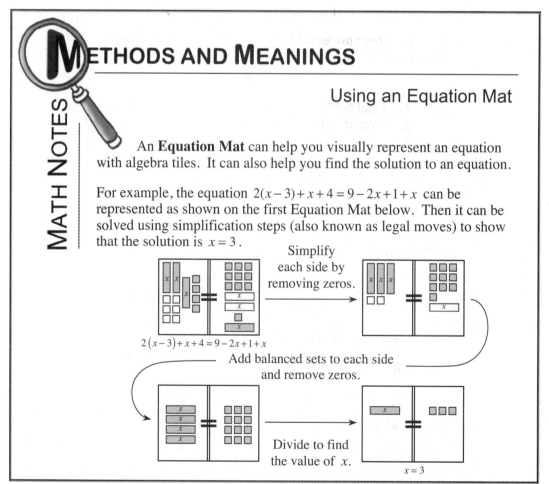

MⒺTHODS AND MEANINGS

Using an Equation Mat

MATH NOTES

An **Equation Mat** can help you visually represent an equation with algebra tiles. It can also help you find the solution to an equation.

For example, the equation $2(x - 3) + x + 4 = 9 - 2x + 1 + x$ can be represented as shown on the first Equation Mat below. Then it can be solved using simplification steps (also known as legal moves) to show that the solution is $x = 3$.

Simplify each side by removing zeros.

$2(x - 3) + x + 4 = 9 - 2x + 1 + x$

Add balanced sets to each side and remove zeros.

Divide to find the value of x.

$x = 3$

6-54.   Consider the Equation Mat at right.

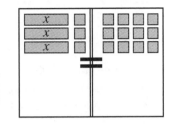

a.   Write the original equation represented.

b.   Simplify the tiles on the mat as much as possible. What value of x will make the two expressions equal?

6-55.   When Lakeesha solved the equation $3(x + 1) = 12$ from problem 6-54, she reasoned this way:

"Since 3 groups of $(x + 1)$ equals 3 groups of 4, then I know that each group of $(x + 1)$ must equal 4."

a.   Do you agree with her reasoning? Explain.

b.   How can the result of Lakeesha's reasoning be written?

c.   Verify that your answer from problem 6-54 will make the equation you wrote in part (b) true.

6-56.   In problems 6-54 and 6-55, $3(x + 1)$ could also be written as $3x + 3$ by using the Distributive Property. The expression $3(x + 1)$ is a product, while $3x + 3$ is a sum. For each expression below, write an equivalent expression that is a product instead of a sum. This process of writing an expression in the form of factors (multiplication) is called **factoring**.

a. $75x - 50$ b. $32x^2 + 48x$ c. $-40m - 30$ d. $63m^2 - 54m$

6-57.   Evaluate the expression $5 + (-3x)$ for the given x-values.

a. $x = 3$ b. $x = \frac{1}{3}$ c. $x = -3$

6-58.   Which fractions below are equivalent? Explain how you know.

A. $\frac{20}{5}$ B. $\frac{-20}{5}$ C. $\frac{20}{-5}$ D. $\frac{-20}{-5}$ E. $-\frac{20}{5}$

6-59.   Simplify each expression.

a. $8.4(7x - 4) + 3.9$

b. $\frac{1}{4} + \frac{4}{5}\left(\frac{3}{4}x - 1\frac{1}{9}\right)$

6.2.2 How do I know that it is correct?

Checking Solutions and the Distributive Property

Sometimes a lot can depend on the solution of a problem. For example, when businesses calculate the cost of packaging and shipping a product, they need to come up with an accurate value. If they miscalculate by only $0.01 per package but ship one million packages per year, this small miscalculation could be costly.

Solving a problem is one challenge. However, once it is solved, it is important to have ways to know whether the solution you found is correct. In this lesson, you will be solving equations and finding ways to determine whether your solution makes the equation true.

6-60. Chen's sister made this riddle for him to solve: *"I am thinking of a number. If you add two to the number then triple it, you get nine."*

a. Build the equation on an Equation Mat. What are *two* ways that Chen could write this equation?

b. Solve the equation and show your work by writing the equation on your paper after each legal move.

c. When Chen told his sister the mystery number in the riddle, she said he was wrong. Chen was sure that he had figured out the correct number. Find a way to justify that you have the correct solution in part (b).

6-61. Now solve the equation $4(x + 3) = 8$. Remember to:

- Build the equation on your Equation Mat with algebra tiles.

- Simplify the equation using your legal moves.

- Record your work on your paper.

- Solve for x. That is, find the value of x that makes the equation true.

6-62. CHECKING YOUR SOLUTION

When you solve an equation that has one solution, you get a value for the variable. But how do you know that you have done the steps correctly and that your answer "works"?

a. Look at your answer for problem 6-61. How could you verify that your solution is correct and convince someone else? Discuss your ideas with your team.

b. When Kelly and Madison compared their solutions for the equation $2x - 7 = -2x + 1$, Kelly got a solution of $x = 2$ and Madison got a solution of $x = -1$. To decide whether the solutions were correct, the girls decided to check their answers to see if they made the expressions equal.

Finish their work below to determine whether either girl has the correct solution.

Kelly's Work	Madison's Work
$2x - 7 \overset{?}{=} -2x + 1$	$2x - 7 \overset{?}{=} -2x + 1$
$2(2) - 7 \overset{?}{=} -2(2) + 1$	$2(-1) - 7 \overset{?}{=} -2(-1) + 1$

c. When checking, Kelly ended up with $-3 = -3$. Does this mean that her answer is correct or incorrect? If it is correct, does this mean the solution is $x = -3$ or $x = 2$? Explain.

d. Go back to problem 6-61 and show how to check your solution for that problem.

6-63. Kelly solved the equation $4(x + 3) = 8$ from problem 6-61. Her work is shown at right.

$$4(x + 3) = 8$$
$$x + 3 = 2$$
$$x + 3 + (-3) = 2 + (-3)$$
$$x = -1$$

a. If $4(x + 3) = 8$, does $x + 3$ have to equal 2? Why?

b. What did Kelly do to remove the 3 unit tiles from the left side of the equation? Does this move affect the equality?

c. If Kelly were solving the equation $3(x - 5) = 9$, what might her first step be? What would she have after that step? You may want to build this equation on an Equation Mat to help make sense of her strategy.

6-64.   Now practice this new solving skill by building each of the equations below with tiles, solving for x, and checking your solution for each equation. Record your work.

a. $4(x+1)+1+(-x)=10+x$

b. $-1+2x-x=x-8+(-x)$

c. $5+2(x-4)=4x+7$

d. $9-3x=1+x$

e. $3x+3-x+2=x+5$

f. $4=3(2x+1)-11$

METHODS AND MEANINGS

MATH NOTES

Equations and Inequalities

Equations always have an equal sign. **Inequalities** have one of inequality symbols defined in the Lesson 6.1.1 Math Note. To **solve** an equation or inequality means to find all values of the variable that make the relationship true. The solution can be shown on a number line. See the examples below.

Solve this equation:
$$x+3=7$$
The solution is:
$$x=4$$

Solve this inequality:
$$x-2<5$$
The solution is:
$$x<7$$

6-65.   Substitute the given solution into the corresponding equation to check it. Then decide if the solution is correct or incorrect.

a. $5x+8=3x-2$ Solution: $x=-5$

b. $2(x+1)+6=20-3x$ Solution: $x=4$

6-66. During this chapter, you will use your new solving skills to solve word problems. Think about and use the strategies you already have to answer the questions below.

a. Andy is 4 years older than Eduardo. If Andy is x years old, write an expression to represent Eduardo's age.

b. In Eduardo's collection, the number of butterflies is 12 more than twice the number of moths. If there are x moths, write an expression to represent the number of butterflies he has.

6-67. Evaluate the expressions $3x - 2$ and $4x + 4$ for the following values of x. When you have found the value for each expression, write a statement using $<$, $>$, or $=$ that shows how the two values are related.

a. $x = 0$ b. $x = -6$ c. $x = 5$ d. $x = -2$

6-68. Victor wants to play "Guess My Number." Use the clues below to figure out his number. Each part is a new game.

a. *"When you double my number and subtract 9, you get my original number. What is my number?"*

b. *"When you double my number and add 5, you get 17. What is my number?"*

6-69. Find the perimeter and area of each triangle below.

a.

14.3 yds   11 yds   12 yds

14 yds

b.

20 ft   12 ft   15 ft

25 ft

6-70. To solve the following problem, use the 5-D Process. Define a variable and write an expression for each column of your table.

In the first three football games of the season, Carlos gained three times as many yards as Alston. Travis gained ten yards more than Carlos. Altogether, the three players gained a total of 430 yards. How many yards did Carlos gain?

6.2.3 How can I record it?

Solving Equations and Recording Work

In this lesson, you will continue to improve your skills of simplifying and solving more complex equations. You will develop ways to record your solving strategies so that another student can understand your steps without seeing your Equation Mat. Consider these questions as you work today:

How can I record the steps I use to solve?

How can I record what is on the Equation Mat after each step?

6-71. Gene and Aidan were using algebra tiles to solve equations. Aidan was called away.

Help Gene finish by completing the table shown below and on the Lesson 6.2.3 Resource Page.

Mat A	Mat B	Steps taken
$2x+2(2x+1)+(-3x)+(-6)$	$4x+3+(-3)+x+8$	Original Equation
		1. Use the Distributive Property.
$3x+(-4)$	$5x+8$	2.
		3. Subtract $3x$ from both sides.
-12	$2x$	4.
		5. Divide both sides by 2.

6-72.   Aidan was frustrated that he needed to write so much when solving an equation. He decided to come up with a shortcut for recording his work to solve a new equation.

As you look at Aidan's recording below of how he solved $2x + 4 = -12$, visualize an Equation Mat with algebra tiles. Then answer the questions for each step below.

a.   What legal move does writing -4 twice represent?

b.   What legal move does circling the $+4$ and the -4 represent?

c.   What does the box around the $\frac{2}{2}$ represent?

d.   Why did Aidan divide both sides by 2?

e.   Check Aidan's solution in the original equation. Is his solution correct?

$$2x + 4 = -12$$
$$-4 \quad\quad -4$$
$$\frac{2x}{2} = \frac{-16}{2}$$
$$x = -8$$

6-73.   The method of recording the steps in the solution of an equation is useful only if you understand what operations are being used and how they relate to the legal moves on your Equation Mat.

Find the work shown at right on your resource page for this lesson.

$$x + (-4) + 6x = 3x - 1 + 5$$

$$-4 + 7x = 3x + 4$$

a.   For each step in the solution, add the missing work below each line that shows what legal moves were used. You may want to build the equation on an Equation Mat.

$$7x = 3x + 8$$

$$4x = 8$$

b.   Check that the solution is correct.

$$x = 2$$

6-74.   For each equation below, solve for x. You may want to build the equation on your Equation Mat. Record your work in symbols using Aidan's method from problem 6-72. Remember to check your solution.

a. $-2x + 5 + 2x - 5 = -1 + (-1) + 6x + 2$

b. $3(4 + x) = x + 6$

6-75. Oliver is building a train depot for his model railroad. As his final step, he needs to apply rain gutters around the roof of the rectangular building. He has 52 cm of rain gutters. The length of the depot is 19 cm. Explore how Oliver can find the width of the depot by answering the questions below.

    a. Find the width of the depot using arithmetic (that is, solve the problem without using any variables). Record your steps.

    b. Use w to represent the width of the depot. Write an algebraic equation that shows the perimeter is 52 cm, and solve your equation. Record your steps.

    c. Which method, the arithmetic or algebraic, did you prefer? Why?

6-76. For each equation below, solve for x. You may want to build the equation on your Equation Mat. Record your work and check your solution.

    a. $5x+(-x)-1=11-2x$

    b. $3(-x+2)+x-1=-x-3$

6-77. Genny is confused. She simplified an equation and ended up with the mat shown at right. What is the value of x?

6-78. Maggie's mom agrees to let Maggie buy small gifts for some of her friends. Each gift costs $4. Maggie's mom gave her a budget of $19. When Maggie went online to order the gifts, she discovered there was a $7 shipping fee no matter how many gifts she bought.

    a. Use arithmetic (without variables) to determine how many gifts Maggie can buy. Record your steps.

    b. Write an algebraic equation to determine how many gifts Maggie can buy with $19, and solve your equation. Record your steps.

    c. Compare and contrast the two methods of solving the problem.

6-79. Your teacher will explain the way you will be working on solving the equations below for x. You may want to build the equations on your Equation Mat. Record your work and check your solution.

    a. $2(x+1)+3=3(x-1)$

    b. $-2x-2=3(-x+2)$

    c. $3+4(2-x)=3x+(-x)-7$

    d. $6(3-x)+(-20)=10+3(4x+2)$

6-80.   LEARNING LOG

In your Learning Log, explain what it means to solve
an equation. What is a solution? Be sure to give an
example. Title this entry "Solving Equations and
Checking Solutions" and include today's date.

Ⓜ️ETHODS AND MEANINGS

Checking a Solution

MATH NOTES

To check a solution to an equation, substitute the solution into
the equation and verify that it makes the two sides of the
equation equal.

For example, to verify that $x = 10$ is a solution to the equation
$3(x-5) = 15$, substitute 10 into the equation for x and then verify
that the two sides of the equation are equal.

As shown at right, $x = 10$ is a
solution to the equation $3(x-5) = 15$.

$$3(10-5) \overset{?}{=} 15$$
$$3(5) \overset{?}{=} 15$$
$$15 = 15 \quad ✓ \quad \textit{True, so x = 10 is a solution.}$$

What happens when you do this
check if your answer is incorrect?
For example, try substituting
$x = 2$ into the same equation. The
result shows that $x = 2$ is not a
solution to this equation.

$$3(2-5) \overset{?}{=} 15$$
$$3(-3) \overset{?}{=} 15$$
$$-9 \neq 15 \quad ✗ \quad \textit{Not true, so x = 2 is not a solution.}$$

Review & Preview

6-81.   Solve each equation below for x. Check your final answer.

a. $4x = 6x - 14$

b. $3x + 5 = 50$

6-82.   Forty percent of the students at Pinecrest Middle School have a school
         sweatshirt. There are 560 students at the school. Draw a diagram to help you
         solve each problem below.

     a.   How many students have a school sweatshirt?

     b.   If 280 students have school t-shirts instead of sweatshirts, what percentage
          of the school has a t-shirt?

     c.   What percentage of the school does not have a t-shirt or a sweatshirt?

6-83.   Latisha wants to get at least a B+ in her history class. To do so, she needs to
         have an overall average of at least 86%. So far, she has taken three tests and
         has gotten scores of 90%, 82%, and 81%.

     a.   Use the 5-D Process to help Latisha determine what percent score she needs
          on the fourth test to get the overall grade that she wants. The fourth test is
          the last test of the grading period.

     b.   The teacher decided to make the last test worth twice as much a regular
          test. How does this change the score that Latisha needs on the last test to
          get an overall average of 86%? Support your answer with mathematical
          work. You may choose to use the 5-D Process again.

6-84.   Factor each expression. That is, write an equivalent expression that is a product
         instead of a sum.

     a. $20y - 84$ b. $24b^2 + 96b$

6-85.   Copy and complete each of the Diamond Problems below.
         The pattern used in the Diamond Problems is shown at right.

     a.   b.   c.   d.

6-86.   A cattle rancher gave $\frac{1}{3}$ of his land to his son and kept the remaining $\frac{2}{3}$ for
         himself. He kept 34 acres of land. How much land did he have to begin with?

6-87.   Solve each equation. Record your work and check your solution.

a. $5(x-2)+(-9)=-7(1-x)$ b. $-6x-7=-1(-9+2x)$

6-88.   Simplify each expression.

a. $\frac{73}{100}\cdot(-\frac{2}{7})$ b. $0.4\cdot0.3$ c. $-\frac{63}{80}+\frac{7}{10}$

d. $5\frac{1}{9}+8\frac{2}{5}$ e. $-\frac{9}{17}-\frac{1}{2}$ f. $-1.2+(-\frac{3}{5})$

6-89.   Sketch the parallelogram shown at right, and then redraw it with sides that are half as long.

a.   Find the perimeters of both the original and smaller parallelograms.

b.   If the height of the original parallelogram (drawn to the side that is 6 units) is 2 units, find the areas of both parallelograms.

6-90.   Evaluate the expression $10-2x$ for the x-values given below.

a. $x=2$ b. $x=\frac{1}{2}$ c. $x=-2$

6-91.   Set up a four quadrant graph and graph the points below to make the four-sided shape $PQRS$.

$P(-2,4)$ $Q(-2,-3)$ $R(2,-2)$ $S(2,3)$

a.   What shape is $PQRS$?   b.   Find the area of the shape.

6-92.   Write and solve an inequality for the following situation.

Robert is painting a house. He has 35 cans of paint. He has used 30 cans of paint on the walls. Now he needs to paint the trim. If each section of trim takes $\frac{1}{2}$ can of paint, how many sections of trim can he paint? Show your answer as an inequality with symbols, in words, and with a number line. Make sure that your solution makes sense for this situation.

6.2.4 How can I represent it?

Using a Table to Write Equations from Word Problems

In the last few lessons, you used algebra tiles and Equation Mats to solve problems in which variables represented specific numbers. The tile and Equation Mat tools are related to the processes you have used to solve word problems in which a specific value is unknown. Today you will connect these two tools and the expressions you wrote using a part of the 5-D Process to extend your repertoire for solving problems.

6-93.   THE 5-D PROCESS REVISITED

Use the 5-D Process to set up the following problem. Complete only *three* trials. Even if you do not yet know the solution, wait for your teacher's instructions.

The Great Lakes contain the largest amount of fresh water on the surface of the planet. Combined, the five lakes (Superior, Michigan, Huron, Erie, and Ontario) contain 84% of North America's and 21% of the world's surface fresh water.

The amount of water in Lake Superior is 1720 cubic miles more than the amount of water in Lake Michigan. Lake Huron has 330 cubic miles of water less than Lake Michigan. If the total amount of water in the three lakes is 4930 cubic miles, how much water is in each lake?

Check the reasonableness of the amounts of water you found for each lake by using estimation strategies: Does the total volume of the three lakes seem reasonable?

6-94.   GO FOR THE GOLD

As you saw in problem 6-93, sometimes organizing
your thinking using the 5-D Process to solve a word
problem involves a lot of work. Sometimes the tables
are very complicated or the numbers require many
trials to find the answer. How can your new
equation-solving skills help you solve word
problems? Read the following word problem and
then answer the questions below.

While looking at the country of Jamaica's results from the 2008 Beijing
Olympics, Gemma noticed that the number of gold medals Jamaica received
was twice the number of silver medals. She also realized that Jamaica received
1 fewer bronze medal than silver medals. Altogether, Jamaica received
11 medals.

a.   Gemma started by setting up the 5-D Process table below. What did she
     define x to represent?

Define			Do	Decide
# Gold	# Silver	# Bronze	Total Number of Medals	11?
$2x$	x	$x-1$		

b.   How did she represent the number of gold and bronze medals?

c.   Write an equation for the total number of medals.

d.   Solve your equation in part (c). What is the value of x? What does this
     represent?

e.   How many gold medals did Jamaica earn? Explain how you know.

6-95.   Solve the following word problems by writing and solving an equation. You may choose to use the 5-D Process and create a table to help you build your equation. It may be helpful first to do one or two trials with numbers to help establish a pattern. Whatever strategy you use, do not forget to define the variable by stating what x represents. Finally, check your answer.

a.   A person's height is positively associated with his or her arm span (the distance between the ends of the fingertips as arms are held out on each side of the body). One of the tallest men in history had an arm span measuring 7 inches more than his height. The combined total of his arm span and height was 221 inches. How tall was this man?

b.   Have you ever tried to hold your breath? Humans can only hold their breath an average of one minute. However, other animals can hold their breath for much longer.

A Greenland whale can hold its breath three times as long as a beaver, and a hippopotamus can hold its breath five minutes less than a beaver. If you added the time a Greenland whale, beaver, and hippopotamus can hold their breath, you would get 95 minutes! How long can a beaver hold its breath?

6-96.   LEARNING LOG

In Chapter 5, you learned about variables and using the 5-D Process to solve problems. In this chapter, you simplified expressions using algebra tiles and focused on solving equations.

In your Learning Log, describe how variables and equations can be used to solve word problems. Use an example problem to help make your explanation clear. Title this entry "Using the 5-D Process to Write and Solve Equations" and label it with today's date.

METHODS AND MEANINGS

MATH NOTES

Defining a Variable

When you write an equation, it is important to **define the variable** carefully. You need to be clear about what you are talking about so that someone else looking at your work understands what the variable represents. This step is an important habit to develop because it is an important step in solving many different math problems.

For example, suppose you have this problem:

At the neighborhood grocery store, grapes cost $3 a pound. If Belinda spent $5.40 on grapes, how many pounds of grapes did she buy?

One equation you could write is $3x = 5.4$, if you know what x stands for. The variable x should be clearly defined, such as $x =$ pounds of grapes, rather than just $x =$ grapes. You could also write $g =$ pounds of grapes, since any letter may be used as a variable.

6-97.   For the end-of-year party, Mt. Rose Middle School ordered 112 pizzas. There were eight fewer veggie pizzas than there were pepperoni pizzas. There were three times as many combo pizzas as pepperoni pizzas. Use the 5-D Process to define a variable and write an equation for this situation. Then determine how many of each kind of pizza were ordered.

6-98.   Consider the equation $7 = 3x - 5$.

a.   Stanley wants to start solving the equation by adding 5 to both sides, while Terrence first wants to subtract 7 from both sides. Will both strategies work? Is one strategy more efficient than the other?

b.   Solve $7 = 3x - 5$. Show your steps.

6-99.   The two triangles at right are similar shapes.

   a. What is the scale factor from shape A to shape B?

   b. Find the missing side lengths.

   c. If you wanted to make shape A smaller instead of bigger, what is a scale factor you could use?

6-100.   Find the area and perimeter of each of the following figures.

   a.

$7\frac{3}{4}$ ft.

$10\frac{1}{5}$ ft.

   b.   square

12.3 mi

   c.

$3\frac{3}{8}$ cm $3\frac{5}{6}$ cm

$4\frac{2}{3}$ cm

   d.

126.57 cm

79.2 cm   85.32 cm

67 cm

6-101.   Factor each expression by writing it as a product instead of a sum.

   a. $90k - 60$

   b. $30d^2 - 18d$

6-102.   Write an expression for each mat at right.

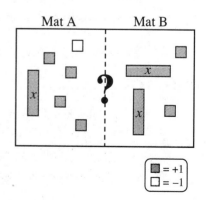

   a. Simplify each mat to determine which expression is greater, if possible.

   b. If $x = 3$, would your answer to part (a) change? Explain.

   c. If $x = -2$, would your answer change? Explain.

6.2.5   How can I model it?

Writing and Solving Equations

Engineers investigate practical problems to improve people's quality of life. To investigate solutions to problems, they often build models. These models can take various forms. For example, a structural engineer designing a bridge might build a small replica of the bridge. Civil engineers studying the traffic patterns in a city might create equations that model traffic flows into and out of a city at different times.

In this lesson, you will be building equations to model and solve problems based on known information. As you work today, keep the following questions in mind.

What does x represent in the equation?

How does the equation show the same information as the problem?

Have I answered the question?

6-103.   Today your team will be responsible for solving a problem and sharing your solution with the class on a poster. It is important that your poster communicates your thinking and reasoning so that people who look at your poster understand how you solved the problem. Your poster should include:

- Connections between the words in the problem and the relationships in your table and/or equation. Connections can be made with arrows, colors, symbols, and/or labels.

- Variables that are defined completely.

- An equation to represent the problem.

- Your solution to the problem.

- The answer declared in a sentence.

- An estimation verifying that the total of your solutions is reasonable.

Begin by solving one of the problems below and writing an equation. Make sure to define the variable you use and answer the question(s) being asked. Using the 5-D Process, including numerical trials, may be helpful.

a.   Hong Kong's tallest building, Two International Finance Center, is 88 stories tall. The former Sears Tower in Chicago is eight stories taller than the Empire State Building in New York City. If all of the buildings were stacked on top of each other, the combined heights would have 300 stories. How many stories does the Sears Tower have?

Problem continues on next page. →

6-103.   *Problem continued from previous page.*

b.   Have you ever driven or walked across a suspension bridge? There are many suspension bridges in the world of different lengths that allow people to travel across rivers, bays, and lakes.

The Mackinac Bridge in Michigan is 1158 meters long. The Tsing Ma Bridge in Hong Kong is 97 meters longer than the Golden Gate Bridge in California. Together, all three bridges have a length of 3815 meters. How long is the Tsing Ma Bridge?

c.   Elevations found in the United States range from California's Death Valley at 282 feet below sea level to Alaska's Mount McKinley, also known as Denali, at 20,320 feet above sea level.

The highest elevation in Delaware is 106 feet higher than the highest elevation in Florida. Louisiana's highest elevation is 190 feet higher than Florida's highest elevation. If you climbed from sea level to the highest points in Delaware, Florida, and Louisiana, you would only climb 1331 feet. How high is the highest elevation in each of the three states?

d.   Most states in the United States are divided into counties. Some counties are very large, while some are very small. Different states have different numbers of counties. Pennsylvania has five less than twice as many counties as Oregon. Florida has one less county than Pennsylvania. Together, the three states have 169 counties. How many counties does each of these three states have?

e.   A train from Washington, D.C. to Chicago stops first in Pittsburgh and then in Cleveland. The distance from Washington, D.C. to Pittsburgh is 30 miles less than twice the distance from Pittsburgh to Cleveland. The distance from Cleveland to Chicago is

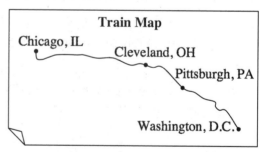

220 miles more than the distance between Pittsburgh and Cleveland. If the entire train ride is 710 miles, how far is the train ride from Cleveland to Chicago?

6-104. Solve the following equations using any method. Show your work and check your solution.

a. $2x+16=5x+4$ b. $3x-5=2x+14$ c. $5x-5=x+15$

6-105. Write an algebraic expression for each situation.

a. Three less than a number.

b. Nine more than three times a number.

c. Two less than five times a number.

6-106. A triangle has a base that is three times longer than its height. It has an area of 486 sq cm.

Use the 5-D Process to find the base and height of the triangle. Write a variable expression for each column of your table.

6-107. Kandi has a bag of marbles. She has 5 black, 3 white, 2 green, and 4 orange marbles. Kandi reaches into the bag without looking and pulls out a marble.

a. What is the probability that she will pull out a green marble?

b. If she does get a green marble and does not put it back in the bag, what is the probability that she will now pull the other green marble from the bag?

c. Assume that Kandi does get the second green marble and does not return it to the bag. What is the probability that she will now pull another green marble from the bag?

6-108. Which of the equations below represent proportional relationships? If the relationship is proportional, identify the constant of proportionality. If the relationship is not proportional, explain why.

a. $y=\frac{3}{4}x+2$ b. $y=\left(4\frac{2}{3}\right)x$ c. $y=3(x-1)$

6-109.   The diagram at right represents an acrobat's sequence of moves on a tightrope, where m represents the distance in feet that she covers each time she does a leap.

a.   How long is each of her leaps? How can you tell?

b.   Write and solve an equation to find the length of each leap.

c.   How long is the tightrope?

6-110.   Solve the following equations using any method. Show your work and check your solution.

a. $3x + 10 = 25$

b. $5(x - 2) = 30$

c. $2x - 9 = x + 7$

6-111.   Use the 5-D Process to solve the following problem. Write an expression to represent each column of your table.

Yosemite Falls, the highest waterfall in the United States, is actually made up of three smaller falls. The Lower Yosemite Falls is 355 feet shorter than the Middle Cascades Falls. The Upper Yosemite Falls is 80 feet more than twice the Middle Cascades Falls. If the entire set of waterfalls is 2425 feet long, how tall is each of the smaller waterfalls?

6-112.   Evaluate the following expressions.

a. $7x + 8$ when $x = 9$

b. $6(y - 11)$ when $y = -6$

c. $45 - 5m + 7$ when $m = -4$

d. $-2t + 9$ when $t = -20$

6-113.   Here are some new distances with given lengths to help Cecil cross the tightrope. Find at least two ways to get Cecil across for each situation. Write your solutions in symbolic form.

a.   Span of tightrope: 19 feet   Given lengths: 4, 5, 7 feet

b.   Span of tightrope: 25 feet   Given lengths: 3, 6, 7 feet

c.   Span of tightrope: 23 feet   Given lengths: 5, 2, 9 feet

6-114.   Walter walked 15.5 blocks from his house to work. It took him 35 minutes. What is his rate in blocks per hour?

6-115.   Jana's mom gave her $100 to shop for some new school clothes. She is at the store and has picked out a pair of pants that cost $49.50. She wants to spend the rest of her money buying various colors of a shirt that is on sale for $12.99. Write an inequality that can be used to calculate the number of shirts she can buy. Solve your inequality. How many shirts can Jana buy?

6.2.6 Is there always a solution?

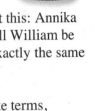

Cases With Infinite or No Solutions

Are all equations solvable? Are all solutions a single number? Think about this: Annika was born first, and her brother William was born 4 years later. How old will William be when Annika is twice his age? How old will William be when Annika is exactly the same as his age?

In this lesson, you will continue to practice your strategies of combining like terms, removing zeros, and balancing to simplify and compare two expressions. You will also encounter unusual situations where the solution may be unexpected. As you work today, focus with your team on these questions:

What if both sides are not equal?

Are there many values of x that will make the expressions equal?

Is there always a solution?

6-116.   Many students believe that every equation has only one solution. However, in the introduction to this lesson you might have noticed that if Annika was four years older than her brother, William, they could never be the same age. Some situations have one solution, others have no solution, and still others have all numbers as solutions.

For each of the following equations, reason with your team to decide if the answer would be "One solution," "No solution," or "All numbers are solutions." If there is a single number solution, write it down. If you are not sure how many solutions there are, have each member of your team try a number to see if you can find a value that makes the equation work.

a. $x = x$

b. $x + 1 = x$

c. $x = 2x$

d. $x + x = 2 + x$

e. $x + x = x - x$

f. $x + x = 2x$

g. $x \cdot x = x^2$

h. $x - 1 = x$

6-117.   Use the 5-D Process to write an equation for the problem below. Then answer the question.

Kelly is 6 years younger than her twin brothers Bailey and Larry. How old will Kelly be when the sum of her brothers ages is 12 more than twice Kelly's?

6-118.   SPECIAL CASES, Part One

Use the equation $8 + x + (-5) = (-4) + x + 7$ to complete parts (a) through (c).

a.   Build the equation on your Equation Mat and simplify it as much as possible. Record your steps and what you see when you have simplified the equation fully. Draw a picture of your final mat.

b.   Have each member of your team test a different value for x in the original equation, such as $x = 0$, $x = 1$, $x = -5$, $x = 10$, etc. What happens in each case?

c.   Are there any solutions to this equation? If so, how many?

6-119.   SPECIAL CASES, Part Two

Use the equation $x + x + 2 = 2x$ to complete parts (a) through (c).

a.   Build the equation on your Equation Mat and simplify it as much as possible. Record your steps and what you see when you have simplified the equation fully. Draw a picture of your final mat.

b.   Have each member of your team test a different value for x in the equation, such as $x = 0$, $x = 1$, $x = -5$, $x = 10$, etc. What happens? Is there a pattern to the results you get from the equation?

c.   Did you find any values for x that satisfied the equation in part (a)? When there is an imbalance of units left on the mat (such as 2 = 0), what does this mean? Is $x = 0$ a solution to the equation?

6-120.   Keeping these special cases in mind, continue to develop your equation-solving strategies by visualizing and solving each equation below. Remember to build each equation on your mat, if needed, to simplify as much as possible, and to solve for x. Identify if one number is the solution, if any number is the solution, or if there is no solution. Record your steps.

a. $-x + 2 = 4$

b. $-3 + x = 2(x + 3)$

c. $5x + 3 + (-x) = 2x + 1 + 2x + 3$

d. $3x + 7 + (-x) + -2 = 2x + 5$

e. $4 + -3x = 2$

f. $3x + 3 = 4 + x + (-1)$

6-121.   **Additional Challenge:** For each of the parts below, create your own equation (involving at least three steps) that has the given solution.

a. $x = -2$

b. $x = \frac{1}{2}$

c.   no solution

d.   all numbers

6-122.   Simplify and solve each equation below for x. Show your work and record your final answer.

a. $24 + 2x = 3x + 2(3 \cdot 4)$

b. $24 + 3x = 3x + 3(7 - 1)$

c. $2(12 + x) = 2x + 24$

6-123.   Show the "check" for each of these problems and write whether the solution is correct or incorrect.

a.   For $3x + 2 = x - 2$, does $x = 0$?

b.   For $3(x - 2) = 30 + x - 2 - x + 2$, does $x = 12$?

6-124.   Some steps in solving an equation are more efficient than others. Complete parts (a) through (d) to determine the most efficient first step to solve the equation $34 = 5x - 21$.

a.   If both sides of the equation were divided by 5, then the equation would be $\frac{34}{5} = x - \frac{21}{5}$. Does this make the problem simpler? Why or why not?

b.   If you subtract 34 from both sides, the equation becomes $0 = 5x - 55$. Does this make the equation simpler to solve? Why or why not?

c.   If you add 21 to both sides, the equation becomes $55 = 5x$. Does this suggestion make this a problem you can solve more easily? Why or why not?

d.   All three suggestions are legal moves, but which method will lead to the most efficient solution? Why?

6-125. Alex has a job delivering newspapers. He puts 20% of his earnings each week into his college savings account. Each week he puts $16 into the account.

a. Draw a diagram to represent this situation. How much money does Alex earn each week?

b. Alex spends 10% of his earnings on snacks each week. How much does he spend?

c. When Alex has worked for one year, he will get a raise that is equal to 15% of his current earnings. How much more money will he earn each week?

6-126. Factor each expression below.

a. $16x - 4$

b. $-10x + 5x^2$

c. $30y - 24x$

6-127. Each of the diagrams below represents a sequence for an acrobat on a tightrope. Each letter represents the unknown length of a trick. For each part below, write and solve an equation to figure out how far the acrobat travels during each trick (that is, the length represented by each letter). Show how you know your answer is correct.

a. Find x.

b. Find j.

c. Find n.

x	7	x

13

j	j	15	j

27

n	n	6	6	6	6

44

6.2.7 Which method should I use?

Choosing a Solving Strategy

Today you will practice writing equations from word problems and solving them using any of the tools you know. You are developing an efficient set of tools to solve any word problem, such as the 5-D Process and algebra tiles. Having a variety of methods will allow you to choose the one that makes sense to you and ultimately makes you a stronger mathematician.

6-128. Nick tried to use a symbolic method to solve $3x - 6 = 27$, but he may have made a mistake. His work is shown at right. If he did make a mistake, on which step did he first make a mistake, and what was his mistake? If he did not make a mistake, check his solution and write "all correct."

$$3x \left(\!- 6\right) = 27$$
$$\underline{\quad\quad +6 \quad\quad +6 \quad}$$
$$\frac{3x}{3} = \frac{33}{3}$$
$$x = 11$$

6-129. Nick represented the equation $3(2x + 4) = -6$ on the Equation Mat at right.

$$\blacksquare = +1$$
$$\square = -1$$

a. Choose a strategy to solve for x. You may continue to use algebra tiles, or you may use symbols on paper.

b. Check your answer. If your answer does not make the equation true, try solving the equation using a different strategy.

6-130.　Read the problem below, and then answer the questions in parts (a) and (b).

Cisco and Misty need to construct a chicken coop for their famous egg-laying hens. The hens need at least 108 square feet of living space. The space available allows Cisco and Misty to make the length of the coop 3 feet longer than the width and to create exactly 108 square feet of area. What are the dimensions of the coop?

a.　Laura tried to use an Equation Mat for this problem but got stuck and decided to use a different strategy. Why do you think she decided not to use the Equation Mat?

b.　Now choose a different method to solve this problem, such as the 5-D Process or writing and solving an equation. Even if you solve an equation and do not use the table from the 5-D Process, you still need to define how you are using variables and remember to write your answer in a sentence. Check your answer.

6-131.　Below is a problem started with a 5-D table.

Describe/Draw:

We want to find the side lengths so the perimeter is 35 m.

	Define			**Do**	**Decide**
	Side 1	Side 2	Side 3	Perimeter	Target: 35 m
Trial 1	5	$5+2=7$	$7+4=11$	$5+7+11=23$	23 *Too small*
	x	$x+2$	$(x+2)+4$	$x+(x+2)+(x+2+4)=35$	

a.　Write the word problem that could have accompanied this 5-D table.

b.　What is your preferred method to solve this problem: algebra tiles, an equation, or the 5-D Process?

c.　Decide on a method to solve this problem, use your method to find your answer, and write a Declare statement for your answer.

6-132.   Apiologists (scientists who study bees) have found
          that the number and types of bees in a hive is based
          on the amount of nectar and pollen available.
          Within a hive are three types of bees that help the
          queen: workers, drones, and nurses.

          In a recent study of a hive, it was found that there
          was a total of 4109 bees, not including the queen.
          There were thirty-three more nurses than drones.
          The number of workers was twelve more than six
          times the number of drones. How many of each
          type of bee was in the hive?

          Choose a method to solve this problem, such as the 5-D Process or writing and
          solving an equation. Even if you solve an equation and do not use the table
          from the 5-D Process, you still need to define how you are using variables and
          remember to write your answer in a sentence. Check your answer with
          estimation to make sure that it is reasonable.

6-133.   Use any method to solve the following equations. Show your work and check
          your solutions.

          a. $3x + 4 = -5$ b. $3(x + 4) = -3$

          c. $3(x + 4) = x + 2(x + 6)$ d. $3x + 4 = 3x - 4$

---------------- Review & Preview ----------------

6-134.   One way of thinking about solving equations is to work to get the variable terms
          on one side of the equation and the constants on the other side. Consider the
          equation $71 = 9x - 37$.

          a.   As a first step, you could subtract 71 from both sides, or divide both sides
                by 9, or add 37 to both sides of the equation. Does one of these steps get all
                of the variable terms on one side of the equation and the constants on the
                other?

          b.   Solve $71 = 9x - 37$ for x. Show your steps.

6-135.   For each equation below, solve for x. Sometimes the easiest strategy is to use
          mental math.

          a. $x - \frac{2}{3} = \frac{1}{3}$ b. $4x = 6$

          c. $x + 4.6 = 12.96$ d. $\frac{x}{7} = \frac{3}{7}$

Core Connections, Course 2

6-136.   Due to differences in gravity, a 100-pound person
          on Earth would weigh about 38 pounds on Mars and
          17 pounds on the moon.

    a.   What would a 150-pound person on Earth
         weigh on Mars? Explain your reasoning with
         words or a diagram.

    b.   What would a 50-pound person on Earth weigh
         on the moon? Explain your reasoning with
         words or a diagram.

    c.   **Additional Challenge:** If an astronaut on the moon weighed about
         34 pounds, what would that astronaut weigh on Mars? Show how you
         know.

6-137.   Evaluate each expression.

    a. $1.2 - 0.8$ b. $-4 - (-2)$ c. $-\frac{6}{11} - (-\frac{1}{4})$

    d. $\frac{2}{3} \cdot \frac{2}{5}$ e. $0.6 \cdot 8$ f. $-\frac{5}{4} \cdot \frac{8}{13}$

6-138.   Rewrite each fraction below as an equivalent fraction, as a decimal, and as a
          percent.

    a. $\frac{6}{18}$ b. $\frac{7}{20}$ c. $\frac{9}{10}$ d. $\frac{4}{25}$

6-139.   This problem is a checkpoint for writing and evaluating algebraic expressions.
          It will be referred to as Checkpoint 6.

          Change each phrase into an algebraic expression.

    a.   Six more than x.   b.   Five less than y.

    c.   Twice a number x, increased by 3.   d.   The product of 5 and y.

    e.   Evaluate each expression in parts (a) through (d) using $x = 5$ or $y = 8$.

          Check your answers by referring to the Checkpoint 6 materials located at the
          back of your book.

          Ideally, at this point you are comfortable working with these types of problems
          and can solve them correctly. If you feel that you need more confidence when
          solving these types of problems, then review the Checkpoint 6 materials and try
          the practice problems provided. From this point on, you will be expected to do
          problems like these correctly and with confidence.

Chapter 6 Closure   What have I learned?

Reflection and Synthesis

The activities below offer you a chance to reflect about what you have learned during this chapter. As you work, look for concepts that you feel very comfortable with, ideas that you would like to learn more about, and topics with which you need more help.

①   SUMMARIZING MY UNDERSTANDING

In this chapter, you have used algebra tiles and an Equation Mat as tools for solving equations. You have also represented your solution steps on an Equation Mat and with algebraic symbols. Today you will use what you have learned about equations in this chapter to show connections between all of these methods. To start, consider the following problem.

Jamee is working to solve an equation. She did the work shown below. With your team, answer the questions that follow:

Jamee's work: Original problem: $3(2x-4)=2(2x+5)$

                               Step 1: $6x-12=4x+10$

                               Step 2: $2x=-2$

- Explain what Jamee did at each step.

- What is her solution?

- Is her solution correct? Justify your answer. If it is not, find her error and the correct answer.

Obtain a Chapter 6 Closure Resource Page (shown at right) from your teacher. Follow the directions below to demonstrate your understanding of solving equations with an Equation Mat, algebraically (with numbers and symbols), and in words.

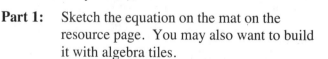

Part 1:   Sketch the equation on the mat on the resource page. You may also want to build it with algebra tiles.

Part 2:   Complete each step to solve the equation. Represent each step on the mat, with symbols, and in words. As you work, ask questions to clarify your thinking and understanding. Make sure you can give reasons for each step.

Part 3:   Color-code the matching steps in each representation. For example, if your second step is to combine like terms, label this step with green in the symbols, on the mat, and in words. Use a new color to code each step.

②   **WHAT HAVE I LEARNED?**

Doing the problems in this section will help you to evaluate which types of problems you feel comfortable with and which ones you need more help with.

Solve each problem as completely as you can. The table at the end of this closure section provides answers to these problems. It also tells you where you can find additional help and where to find practice problems like them.

CL 6-140.   Consider the Equation Mat at right.

    a.   Write the original equation represented.

    b.   Simplify as needed. Record all steps of your work. What value of x will make the two sides equal?

    c.   Check your solution.

CL 6-141.   Write the expressions for the Expression Mats at right.

    a.   Simplify each mat to determine which side is greater.

    b.   If $x = 4$, would your answer to part (a) change? Explain.

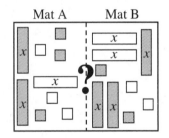

CL 6-142.   Serena found the spinner at right. Help her find the probability of spinning each of the following colors on the spinner.

    a.   What is the P(yellow or blue)?

    b.   What is the P(not red)?

    c.   What is the P(green)?

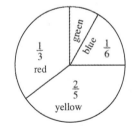

CL 6-143. The shapes at right are similar.

a. What is the scale factor from shape A to shape B?

b. What are the lengths of the missing sides?

CL 6-144. Solve this problem by using the 5-D Process or writing and solving an equation. No matter which you method you use, be sure to define your variable and write an equation to represent the relationship.

A rectangle has a perimeter of 30 inches. Its length is one less than three times its width. What are the length and width of the rectangle?

CL 6-145. Kindra would like to have at least $1500 in her savings account.

a. If she starts with $61 in her savings account, write an inequality to show how much she wants to have.

b. How much does Kindra need to save? Show your solution as an inequality with symbols, in words, and on a number line.

CL 6-146. Alejandra has been practicing her free-throw shots as she gets ready for basketball season. At her last practice, she made 70% of her shots from the free-throw line. If she shot the ball 130 times:

a. How many times did she make a free-throw?

b. How many times did she miss? What percentage of her shots did she miss?

CL 6-147. Copy and complete each of the Diamond Problems below. The pattern used in the Diamond Problems is shown at right.

CL 6-148.   Simplify each expression.

a. $\frac{3}{8}+(-\frac{4}{6})-\frac{1}{3}$

b. $-\frac{5}{7}+\frac{4}{9}-(-\frac{2}{3})$

c. $\frac{2}{5}\cdot\frac{3}{8}-\frac{3}{4}$

d. $-\frac{6}{11}+(-\frac{2}{3})-\frac{5}{6}$

e. $-\frac{2}{3}\cdot\left(2\frac{1}{4}\right)\cdot\frac{3}{4}$

f. $\frac{5}{7}+(-\frac{1}{3})-(-\frac{1}{2})$

CL 6-149.   For each of the problems above, do the following:

- Draw a bar or number line that represents 0 to 10.

- Color or shade in a portion of the bar that represents your level of understanding and comfort with completing that problem on your own.

If any of your bars are less than a 5, choose *one* of those problems and do one of the following tasks:

- Write two questions that you would like to ask about that problem.
- Brainstorm two things that you DO know about that type of problem.

If all of your bars are a 5 or above, choose one of those problems and do one of these tasks:

- Write two questions you might ask or hints you might give to a student who was stuck on the problem.
- Make a new problem that is similar and more challenging than that problem and solve it.

WHAT TOOLS CAN I USE?

You have several tools and references available to help support your learning: your teacher, your study team, your math book, and your Toolkit, to name only a few. At the end of each chapter, you will have an opportunity to review your Toolkit for completeness. You will also revise or update it to reflect your current understanding of big ideas.

The main elements of your Toolkit should be your Learning Logs, Math Notes, and the vocabulary used in this chapter. Math words that are new appear in bold in the text. Refer to the lists provided below and follow your teacher's instructions to revise your Toolkit, which will help make it useful for you as you complete this chapter and as you work in future chapters.

Learning Log Entries

- Lesson 6.1.2 – Simplifying Expressions (Legal Moves)
- Lesson 6.1.4 – Finding Boundary Points
- Lesson 6.2.3 – Solving Equations and Checking Solutions
- Lesson 6.2.4 – Using the 5-D Process to Write and Solve Equations

Math Notes

- Lesson 6.1.1 – Inequality Symbols
- Lesson 6.1.3 – Algebra Vocabulary
- Lesson 6.1.4 – Graphing Inequalities
- Lesson 6.2.1 – Using an Equation Mat
- Lesson 6.2.2 – Equations and Inequalities
- Lesson 6.2.3 – Checking a Solution
- Lesson 6.2.4 – Defining a Variable
- Lesson 6.2.6 – Solutions to an Equation With One Variable

Core Connections, Course 2

Mathematical Vocabulary

The following is a list of vocabulary found in this chapter. Some of the words have been seen in the previous chapter. The words in bold are words that are new to this chapter. Make sure that you are familiar with the terms below and know what they mean. For the words you do not know, refer to the glossary or index. You might also add these words to your Toolkit so that you can reference them in the future.

5-D Process	**boundary point**	**coefficient**
constant term	Distributive Property	equation
Equation Mat	evaluate	expression
Expression Comparison Mat	**factor**	**factoring**
inequality	**inequality symbols**	proportional relationship
ratio	**solution**	simplify
term	variable	

Answers and Support for Closure Problems
What Have I Learned?

Note: MN = Math Note, LL = Learning Log

Problem	Solution	Need Help?	More Practice
CL 6-140.	a. $3x + 2 = x - 2$ b. $x = -2$ c. $3(-2) + 2 = -2 - 2$ $-6 + 2 = -4$ $-4 = -4$	Lessons 6.2.1, 6.2.2, and 6.2.3 MN: 6.2.1, 6.2.2, 6.2.3, and 6.2.6 LL: 6.1.2 and 6.2.3	Problems 6-54, 6-81, 6-98, 6-104, 6-110, 6-122, and 6-129
CL 6-141.	a. $x = x$, The mats are equal in value. b. No, the mats will be equal for any value of x.	Lessons 6.1.1 and 6.1.2 MN: 6.1.1 LL: 6.1.2	Problems 6-17 and 6-102

Problem	Solution	Need Help?	More Practice
CL 6-142.	a. P(yellow or blue) $= \frac{2}{5} + \frac{1}{6} = \frac{17}{30}$ b. P(not red) $= 1 - \frac{1}{3} = \frac{2}{3}$ c. P(green) $= 1 - \frac{1}{3} - \frac{2}{5} - \frac{1}{6} = \frac{1}{10}$	Lessons 1.2.2 and 5.2.3 MN: 1.2.3 and 5.2.5 LL: 5.2.3	Problems CL 5-151 and 6-107
CL 6-143.	a. $\frac{1}{4}$ b. On shape A, the missing sides are 10 and 8 feet; on shape B, the missing sides are 2 and 1.5 feet.	Lesson 4.1.1 MN: 4.1.2	Problems CL 4-125, 5-22, 5-142, and 6-99
CL 6-144.	The length is 11 in. and the width is 4 in. If x = width, one possible equation would be $x + (3x - 1) + x + (3x - 1) = 30$.	Lessons 5.3.2, 5.3.3, and 6.2.4 MN: 5.3.3 and 6.2.4 LL: 5.3.4 and 6.2.4	Problems CL 5-150, 6-70, 6-83, 6-97, 6-106, and 6-111
CL 6-145.	a. $\$61 + x \geq \$1500$ b. $x \geq \$1439$; She needs to save more than or equal to \$1439. 	Lessons 6.1.3 and 6.1.4 MN: 6.1.1, 6.1.4, and 6.2.2 LL: 6.1.4	Problems 6-29, 6-42, 6-92, and 6-115
CL 6-146.	a. 91 b. 39 shots, 30%	Lessons 5.1.1 and 5.1.2 MN: 5.1.2	Problems CL 5-149, 6-22, 6-32, 6-82, and 6-125
CL 6-147.	a. $\frac{15}{8}$ and $3\frac{1}{12}$ b. 3 and $6\frac{1}{2}$ c. -12 and 2 d. 16 and -3	Problem 2-16	Problems CL 4-123 and 6-85
CL 6-148.	a. $-\frac{15}{24} = -\frac{5}{8}$ b. $\frac{25}{63}$ c. $-\frac{24}{40} = -\frac{3}{5}$ d. $-\frac{135}{66} = -2\frac{1}{22}$ e. $-\frac{9}{8} = -1\frac{1}{8}$ f. $\frac{37}{42}$	Lessons 1.2.6, 2.2.5, and 2.2.6 MN: 2.2.5 and 2.3.1 LL: 1.2.8	Problems CL 5-155, 6-8, and 6-88

Proportions and Percents

7

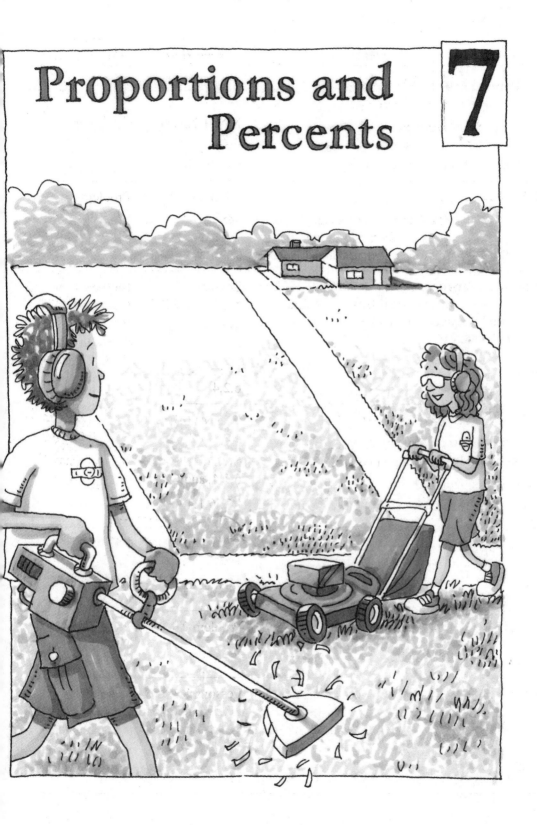

CHAPTER 7

When traveling in a car, have you ever asked, *"When are we going to get there?"* Did you know that you could use mathematics to answer that question? In Section 7.1, you will use diagrams, like the ones you used for percents, to find the relationship between rate, time, and distance.

Then you will revisit scale factors and connect them to percents. You will learn how to simplify difficult problems by rewriting equations to remove fractional and decimal coefficients. Finally, you will investigate how to find the percent increase, percent decrease, and simple interest.

Guiding Questions

Think about these questions throughout this chapter:

How is it changing?

What is the relationship?

What is the connection?

How can I represent it?

What strategy should I use?

You have studied many different proportional relationships, including scale drawings, unit pricing, penny towers, and gas mileage. You will explore more about proportional relationships in Section 7.2 as you learn additional strategies for solving them.

In this chapter, you will learn how to:

> ➤ Solve problems involving distance, rate, and time.
> ➤ Solve equations that have fractional or decimal coefficients.
> ➤ Find the whole amount if you only know a percentage of it, and vice versa.
> ➤ Calculate simple interest.
> ➤ Set up and solve proportional equations.

Chapter Outline

Section 7.1 You will identify the relationship between distance, rate, and time and will use it to solve word problems. You will connect your work with percents and scale factors to solve new problems involving part-whole relationships. You will also develop strategies to solve equations with fractional and decimal coefficients. Finally, you will explore percent change and simple interest.

Section 7.2 This section reviews and extends the idea of proportional relationships that you studied in Chapter 4. You will learn new strategies for solving proportional situations.

7.1.1 What is the relationship?

Distance, Rate, and Time

In this course, you have looked at several relationships between two sets of information and investigated how one piece of information can or cannot be found from the other. To continue your investigation of proportional relationships from Chapter 4, you will look at the mathematical relationship between distance, rate, and time. Later, in the final section of this chapter, you will identify proportional relationships and use your understanding of proportionality to solve problems.

7-1. George stood on the train platform and waved goodbye to his sister as she left for summer camp. Later, as he was getting in his car to drive home, he saw a light flashing inside the train station and heard an announcement that his sister's train had malfunctioned and was stuck on the tracks. George had a map of the train's route and decided to drive to where the train was stuck and pick up his sister.

How can he figure out where the train is? What information would help him to figure it out? Be prepared to share your ideas with the class.

7-2. TOYS

If you needed to predict how far a car, train, or plane had gone, it would be helpful to know something about how fast it was going and how long it had been moving. You will work with your team to investigate the relationship between distance, speed (or rate), and time in the following experiment.

Problem continues on next page. →

7-2.   *Problem continued from previous page.*

Obtain a meter stick, a toy (such as a wind-up car), a long piece of
paper, and a stopwatch from your teacher. Put the paper on the floor,
draw a starting line near one end of it, and place the toy on the edge
of the paper facing the starting line as shown at right. Place the toy a
short distance behind the starting line so that it can reach a constant
speed by the time it gets to the starting line.

Read the directions below for taking data *before* starting your toy.

Directions for Taking Data

1. Appoint a Timer, a Toy-starter, a Marker, and a Measurer.

2. The Toy-starter should start the toy.

3. As the front end of the toy reaches the starting line, the Timer should
    start the stopwatch.

4. When five seconds have passed, the Timer calls out "Now." At this
    moment, the Marker makes a mark (without touching the toy) at the
    place on the paper where the front end of the toy is. This process repeats
    at ten seconds, fifteen seconds, etc. for at least twenty seconds or until
    the toy has reached the end of the paper.

5. The Measurer measures each distance in centimeters *from the starting
    line*.

---

a. Do a "dry run" of the experiment one time *without collecting data*, and talk
    with your team about how, exactly, you will collect the data.

b. Work with your team to take data comparing the time that has passed (in
    seconds) to the distance (in cm) that the toy is from the starting line,
    following the directions above.

c. Obtain a Lesson 7.1.1 Resource Page from your teacher. Work with your
    team to organize your data into a table and graph it. Be prepared to share
    your table and graph with the class. Then think about the following
    questions.

    i. Where does your graph begin? Should your graph "stop"? Would it
        make sense to continue your graph to show how your toy would travel
        if you were to continue measuring for more time?

    ii. How far would you expect your toy to have traveled after 7 seconds
        have passed? What about after 2.3 seconds? Does it make sense to
        connect the points on the graph? Why or why not?

7-3.   What is the unit rate of your toy? That is, approximately how far does your toy travel each second? How can you see this in your table? How can you see it on your graph? Be prepared to explain your ideas to the class.

7-4.   How can you use your answer to problem 7-3 to write an equation relating the time the car has been moving to the distance it has traveled? Work with your team to write an equation relating distance and time.

7-5.   If your toy were twice as fast, how far would it travel each second? How would you see this in the table? How would you see it on the graph? Again, be prepared to explain your ideas to the class.

7-6.   If your toy travels at a constant speed, then the distance your toy has traveled and the time it has taken are related to each other proportionally. In a **proportional relationship**, two quantities are related by a **constant of proportionality** (or a **constant multiplier**). For your toy, the constant of proportion is called the **rate**. In this case, it is also the speed.

        Where else in this course have you seen two quantities related by a constant multiplier? Work with your team to come up with examples of proportional relationships and be ready to contribute your ideas to the class discussion.

7-7.   Answer each of the following questions and be ready to explain how you could use your table or graph to get each answer.

        a.   What distance would your toy travel in 9 seconds?

        b.   How far would your toy travel in 25 seconds?

        c.   How many seconds would it take your toy to travel 300 cm?

7-8.   Bella wants to use her toy car to deliver a secret note to Edward, who is sitting all the way across the cafeteria, approximately 20 meters from her. She plans to get the car started and then leave the cafeteria so Edward will not see her. If her car travels at 1.1 meters per second, about how much time will she have to get out of the cafeteria before Edward gets the note?

7-9.   **Additional Challenge:** Gloria and David's toys crossed the starting line at exactly the same time and are traveling in the same direction. Gloria's toy travels at 40 centimeters per second, and David's toy travels 35 centimeters per second. After 20 seconds, how far apart will their toys be? Be prepared to explain your thinking to the class.

MATH NOTES

METHODS AND MEANINGS

Histograms and Stem-and-Leaf Plots

A **histogram** is similar to a bar graph in that each bar represents data in an interval of numbers. The intervals for the data are shown on the horizontal axis, and the frequency (number of pieces of data in each interval) is represented by the height of a bar above the interval.

The labels on the horizontal axis represent the lower end of each interval. For example, the histogram at right shows that 10 students take at least 15 minutes but less than 30 minutes to get to school.

Histograms are used to display numeric data with an order, while bar graphs display data in categories where order generally does not matter.

A **stem-and-leaf plot** shows the same data as a histogram, but it shows the individual values from a set of data and how the values are distributed. The "stem" part of the graph represents all of the digits in a number except the last one. The "leaf" part of the graph represents the last digit of each of the numbers.

Example: Students in a math class received the following scores on their tests: 49, 52, 54, 58, 61, 61, 67, 68, 72, 73, 73, 73, 78, 82, and 83. Display the test score data on a stem-and-leaf plot.

7-10. It took Ivan $7\frac{1}{2}$ hours to drive 412.5 miles at a constant speed. How fast was he driving? Show how you know.

7-11. Make a graph to show the relationship between distance and time for a bicycle that travels 10 miles every hour.

7-12. Twenty-five percent of the students at Marcus Garvey Middle School bring their lunches from home. 225 students do not bring their lunch. How many students attend the school? Draw and label a diagram to show the number and percent of each group of students.

7-13. Copy and rewrite the following expressions by combining like terms, making zeros, and using the Distributive Property. Visualizing the expressions by using algebra tiles may be helpful.

a. $(-3)+4x+2+2x+2x$

b. $-8x+4+(-3)$

c. $7x^2+3x+4+7x^2+3x+4$

d. $5(x-4)$

7-14. Sao can text 1500 words per hour. He needs to text a message with 85 words. He only has 5 minutes between classes to complete the text. Can he do it in 5 minutes?

7-15. Find the new dimensions of the figure given at right when it is enlarged by a scale factor of 2.5. Then find the perimeter and area of the original and enlarged figures.

7.1.2 How can I make it smaller or bigger?

Scaling Quantities

In Chapter 5, you learned how to find the percent of a number by making a diagram to relate the part to the whole and find the desired portion. This calculation is fairly straightforward if the percent is a multiple of 10, like 40%, or can be thought of as a fraction, like $\frac{1}{4} = 25\%$. However, it can be more challenging if the percent is something like 6.3% or 84.5%.

Today you will connect what you have learned previously about the relationship between distance, rate, and time to the idea of scale factors. You will learn how to use a scale factor to find the corresponding lengths of similar figures. This idea will add a powerful new tool to your collection of problem-solving strategies that will help you to calculate percents.

7-16. Dana is training for a bicycle race. He can ride his bike 25 miles per hour.

One day, when he had been riding for $\frac{3}{5}$ of an hour, he had to stop and fix a flat tire. How many miles had he ridden when he stopped? The diagram below may be useful.

7-17. Matt thought about problem 7-16 and drew the diagram at right. Look at Matt's drawing and decide how he is thinking about this problem.

25 miles   Original $\cdot \frac{3}{5} \Rightarrow$ x New

a. Write an equation that uses the scale factor to find x.

b. What connection is Matt making between finding a distance using the rate and time (as you did in problem 7-16) and using a scale factor with similar figures? How are the situations alike and how are they different?

     Core Connections, Course 2

7-18. In the two previous problems, $\frac{3}{5}$ is used in two ways: first, as *time* in the rate problem $\frac{25 \text{ miles}}{1 \text{ hr}} \cdot \frac{3}{5}$ hrs , and second, as the *scale factor* in the similar triangle problem used to find three fifths of 25 miles. Both of these situations resulted in an equivalent calculation: $25 \cdot \frac{3}{5} = 15$. How else could this be written?

a. Using the portions web shown at right, work with your team to find two other ways to write the equation $25 \cdot \frac{3}{5} = 15$. For example, one way might be $25 \cdot \frac{6}{10} = 15$.

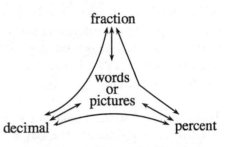

Representations of a Portion

b. If you did not already find it, what percent would be equivalent to $\frac{3}{5}$? Use this percent to write a statement in words and symbols that is equivalent to $25 \cdot \frac{3}{5} = 15$.

c. Use the idea of scaling to find the following values. Write an expression using either a fraction or a percent, and then find the result.

    i.   90% of 25 miles   *ii.* 8% of $75   *iii.* 25% of 144

7-19. Josea went out to dinner at an Indian restaurant. The total bill was $38. She wanted to leave a 15% tip.

a. If you use the idea of scaling to find the tip amount, what would she need to multiply by? As you talk about this with your team, consider:

- How could you represent this multiplier as a fraction?

- How could you represent it as a decimal?

- Does it make a difference which representation, fraction or decimal, you use to solve this problem?

- Which do you think will be easier?

b. How much should Josea leave for the tip? Show your calculations.

c. If Josea changes her mind and wants to leave a 20% tip instead, how much will this be?

7-20. While shopping for a computer game, Isaiah found one that was on sale for 35% off. He was wondering if he could use $\frac{35}{100}$ as a multiplier to scale down the price to find out how much he would have to pay for the game.

a. If Isaiah uses $\frac{35}{100}$ as a scale factor (multiplier), will he find the price that he will pay for the game? Why or why not?

b. There is scale factor (multiplier) other than 35% that can be used to find the sale price. What is it? Draw a diagram to show how this scale factor is related to 35%. Label the parts of your diagram "discount" and "sale price" along with the relevant percents.

c. How much will Isaiah have to pay for the game if the original price is $40? Show your strategy.

METHODS AND MEANINGS

Quartiles and Interquartile Range (IQR)

Quartiles are points that divide a data set into four equal parts (and thus, the use of the prefix "quar" as in "quarter"). One of these points is the median, which you learned about in Chapter 1, since it marks the middle of the data set. In addition, there are two other quartiles in the middle of the lower and upper halves: the **first quartile** and the **third quartile**.

Suppose you have this data set: 22, 43, 14, 7, 2, 32, 9, 36, and 12.

To find **quartiles**, the data set must be placed in order from smallest to largest. Then divide the data set into two halves by finding the median of the entire data set. Next find the median of the lower and upper halves of the data set. (Note that if there are an odd number of data values, the median is not included in either half of the data set.) See the example below.

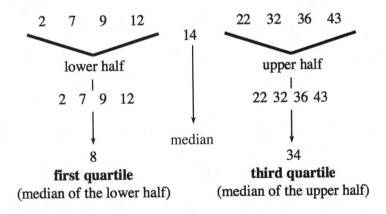

The **interquartile range** (**IQR**) is one way (along with range) to measure the spread of the data. Statisticians often prefer using the IQR to measure spread, because it is not affected much by outliers or non-symmetrical distributions. The IQR is the range of the middle 50% of the data. It is calculated by subtracting the first quartile from the third quartile. In the above example, the IQR is 26 (34 − 8 = 26).

7-21.   Ameena's boat travels 35 miles per hour. The best fishing spot in the lake is
27 miles away from her starting point.

a.   If she drives her boat for $\frac{2}{3}$ of an hour, will she make it to the best fishing
spot on the lake?

b.   How long will Ameena need to drive to get to the best fishing spot on the
lake? Express your answer in both a portion of an hour and in minutes.

7-22.   Use the triangles below right to answer the questions that follow.

a.   What is the scale factor from A to B?

b.   What is the scale factor from B to A?

c.   What is the relationship of the scale factors?

7-23.   Simplify each expression.

a. $\frac{1}{2}x + \frac{7}{12} + \frac{3}{5}x - \frac{2}{3}$

b. $5.3 - 2.8x - 7.1 + 3.9x$

7-24.   Copy the diagram below on your paper. Use the given information to fill in all
of the missing labels.

0%   ? students   28 students
                                                          ?

0%   100%
        60%   ? %

7-25.   Alan is making a bouquet to take home to his grandmother. He needs to choose one kind of greenery and one kind of flower for his bouquet. He has a choice of ferns or leaves for his greenery. His flower choices are daisies, carnations, and sunflowers.

  a. Draw a tree diagram to show the different bouquets he could make. How many are there?

  b. What is the probability that he will use ferns?

  c. What is the probability that he will not use sunflowers?

  d. What is the probability that he will use leaves and carnations?

7-26.   Read the Math Notes box in this lesson and use the information to complete the following problems.

The daily high temperatures in degrees Fahrenheit for the last two weeks in Grand Forks, North Dakota were 7, 1, –3, 0, 4, –1, 2, 5, 7, 7, 3, –2, –4, and –5.

  a. Calculate the median temperature.

  b. Find the first and third quartiles (Q1 and Q3).

  c. What is the interquartile range (IQR)?

7.1.3   Which multiplier should I use?

Solving Problems Involving Percents

As you have seen many times in this course, there is usually more than one way to solve a problem. When a problem uses portions (fractions, decimals, or percents), there are different ways to write the numbers and different solving strategies to choose from. Today you will look at the different multipliers that can scale a quantity and see what each of them will help you find. As you work with your team today, consider the questions below.

What multiplier (scale factor) should I use?

How can I write an equation?

7-27.   Hugo and his family were shopping and purchased a new bed. The bed was a great deal at 60% off of the original cost. The bed originally cost $245.

a.   Draw a diagram for this situation.

b.   If Hugo scales (multiplies) the original price of the bed by 60%, what will his result represent?

c.   What should Hugo scale (multiply) the original price by to find the new price of the bed?

d.   Work with your team to find the sale price of the bed in two different ways, that is, using two different multipliers (scale factors). How do your answers from your two methods compare?

7-28.   Hugo's older sister, Sandra, had the same summer job for the past two years. Last year, she worked the entire summer and was paid a salary of $3,000. This summer, she is going to get a 6% raise in pay. To figure out how much she will make, Sandra drew the following diagram.

a.   Copy the diagram on your paper and fill in the missing information.

b.   Since Sandra's salary is increasing, does it make sense that her scale factor (multiplier) should be less than 1, equal to 1, or more than 1? Why?

c.   The diagram shows Sandra's original salary and the amount of the increase. What is the scale factor (multiplier) between her original salary and her new salary? That is, what number could Sandra multiply the original salary by to get the new salary?

d.   Show two ways that use different scale factors (multipliers) that Sandra can use to compute her new salary.

7-29.   Miranna teaches gymnastics lessons at summer camp. She is paid $12.50 per hour.

a.   If Miranna were offered a raise of 100% per hour, what would her new hourly rate be? What percent of her original pay would she be paid?

b.   Miranna is offered a raise of 75% of her hourly rate to teach a private lesson. How much per hour would she be paid for the private lesson? What percent of her original pay would she get?

c.   What is the relationship between the percent raise that Miranna gets and her new pay as a percent of her original pay? How is this related to the scale factor (multiplier) between her original pay and her new pay?

7-30. Liam was working on a problem and drew a diagram like the one below. He then wrote the equation $(\$72)(0.14) = x$. Does his equation agree with his diagram?

- If you agree, then solve his equation for x.

- If you disagree, write and solve a new equation that will find x in his diagram.

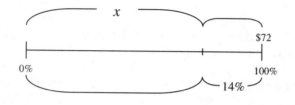

7-31. **Additional Challenge:** Ramon went to the corner store and bought more notebook paper to do his homework. The cost for the paper was $7.50, but he also had to pay the 8.1% sales tax. How much will the notebook paper cost Ramon? If Ramon gives the clerk $10, how much change should he receive?

7-32. LEARNING LOG

In your Learning Log, describe how you scale a quantity. For example, how do you know what multiplier (scale factor) to use? How can you tell if your multiplier should be more than one? Title your entry "Scaling Quantities" and include today's date.

MＥTHODS AND MＥANINGS

Describing Data Distributions

Distributions of data are typically described by considering the **center**, **shape**, **spread**, and **outliers**.

Center: The median best represents the center (or a "typical" data value) if the distribution is not symmetrical or if there are outliers. Either the mean or the median is appropriate for describing the center of symmetrical distributions with no outliers.

Shape: The shape is the overall appearance of the data when it is displayed in a histogram or stem-and-leaf plot. Is the distribution fairly symmetrical? Uniform? Single peaked? Skewed? Does it have large gaps or clusters?

Spread: Spread is a measure of the variability of the data, that is, how much scatter there is in the data. For non-symmetrical data or data with outliers, use the interquartile range (IQR) to describe the spread, since it is based on median. For symmetrical data with no outliers, either the mean absolute deviation, which is based on the mean, or the IQR are appropriate measures of spread. The range is not usually the best measure of the scatter in data, because it considers only the maximum and the minimum values and not what is occurring in between.

Outliers: An outlier is any data point that is far removed from the bulk of the rest of the data.

7-33.   A homeowner must reduce the use of his home's electricity. The home currently consumes 25.7 kwh (kilowatt hours) of electricity per day, and the homeowner must reduce the use by 20%. Find the amount of electricity that will be used after the reduction in two different ways, using two different scale factors.

7-34.   Copy and simplify the following expressions by combining like terms, making zeros, and using the Distributive Property. Using algebra tiles may be helpful.

   a. $(-1) + 4x + 2 + 2x + x$ b. $-8x + 4 + (-3) + 10x$

   c. $(-4) + 1x^2 + 3x + 4$ d. $2(3x - 2)$

7-35.   Study the following division problems and the diagrams that represent them. Answer the question below each diagram.

   a. $8 \div \frac{1}{3}$ b. $8 \div \frac{1}{4}$

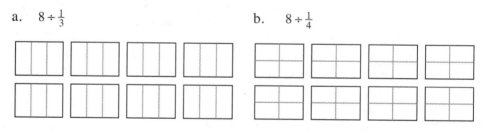

        How many thirds?   How many fourths?

7-36.   The table at right shows speed limits in some foreign countries in kilometers per hour. One kilometer is equal to 0.6 miles. What are these speed limits in miles per hour?

Speed Limits in km per hour		
Country	Country Roads	Motorways
Australia	100	110
South Africa	100	120
Great Britain	96	112
Turkey	90	90

7-37.   Simplify each expression.

a. $18 \div \frac{3}{4}$

b. $\frac{2}{3}(9-6)+40$

c. $15 \div 5 + \frac{1}{2} \cdot \left(-\frac{4}{7}\right)$

d. $-\frac{7}{10}+\left(-\frac{5}{12}\right)-\left(\frac{1}{4}\right)$

e. $4.25-7.06$

f. $\frac{7}{8}-\left(-\frac{1}{10}\right)+\left(-\frac{3}{5}\right)$

7-38.   Read the Math Notes boxes in this lesson and in the previous lesson. Use the information to complete the following problems.

The coach of the girls' basketball team weighed each player. Their weights in pounds were 120, 122, 126, 130, 133, 147, 115, 106, 120, 112, and 142.

a.   Make a stem-and-leaf plot of the team players' weights.

b.   Make a histogram of the teams' weights.

c.   Describe the shape and spread of the data. That is, is it symmetric or non-symmetric? Does it have more than one peak or only one? Is it tightly packed together or widely spread out?

d.   Does this data have any outliers? Which measure of center, mean or median, would be appropriate to use to describe the typical weight?

e.   What is the typical weight of a player on the team?

f.   What is the range of the data?

7.1.4 How can I solve it?

Equations with Fraction and Decimal Coefficients

Throughout this course, you have worked with quantities represented in multiple ways. You have seen that $\frac{12}{16}$, 0.75, 75%, and $\frac{3}{4}$ each represent the same portion even though they *look* different. In your work with algebra tiles, you visualized and described perimeters in different ways. For example, the perimeter of the algebra tiles at right can be described by the expressions $3x + 2 + x$, $x + 1 + x + 1 + x + x$, or $4x + 2x + 2 - 2x$ units.

In this lesson, you will develop strategies to solve a new type of equation: equations with coefficients that are fractions. Recall that coefficients are the numerical part of a term, such as the 5 in $5x$ and the $\frac{2}{3}$ in $\frac{2}{3}x^2$. You will choose between different strategies based on how the problem is represented, what diagram you draw, or whether you represent the situation with an equation. As you explore solving strategies today, keep these questions in mind:

How can I represent it?

How are the representations related?

What is the best approach for this equation?

7-39.   ARE WE THERE YET?

The Sutton family took a trip to see the mountains in Rocky Mountain National Park. Linda and her brother, Lee, kept asking, *"Are we there yet?"* At one point, their mother answered, *"No, but what I can tell you is that we have driven 100 miles and we are about $\frac{2}{5}$ of the way there."*

Linda turned to Lee and asked, *"How long is this trip, anyway?"* They each started thinking about whether they could determine the length of the trip from the information they were given.

Linda's Method

Lee's Method

Problem continues on next page. →

7-39.   *Problem continued from previous page.*

   a. Explain how both Linda's work and Lee's work illustrate the situation described by their mother. What does x represent in each diagram?

   b. What equation could represent this situation? Use the scale factor (multiplier) to represent this situation in an equation. Let x represent the total distance in miles.

   c. Is the answer going to be more or less than 100 miles? Explain your thinking.

7-40.   Linda remarked to Lee, *"When I look at my diagram, I see that the total distance is two-and-a-half times the distance we've driven."*

   a. Do you agree? How can you add labels to Linda's diagram to show $2\frac{1}{2}$ times the distance?

   b. How long is the trip? Show how you know.

7-41.   Lee thinks what he knows about similar triangles can help.

   a. Review problem 7-22, which involved similar triangles. How are the scale factors related?

   b. How can the relationship of the scale factors between similar shapes help Lee? Find the missing scale factor in his diagram at right. That is, what could he multiply 100 by to solve for x?

   c. Use the new scale factor to find x. Does your answer agree with the one you found in part (b) of problem 7-40?

7-42. As Linda and Lee were talking about the problem (from problem 7-39), their mother overheard and offered them another strategy: *"Here is how I would start solving the problem."* She showed them the work at right.

$$\frac{2}{5}x = 100$$

$$\frac{\frac{2}{5}x}{\frac{2}{5}} = \frac{100}{\frac{2}{5}}$$

   a. *"I see a Giant One!"* exclaimed Lee. Where is the Giant One? Help rewrite the left side of the equation.

   b. One way of making sense of $\dfrac{100}{\frac{2}{5}}$ is as $100 \div \frac{2}{5} = ?$.

   This could be read, *"How many two fifths are in one hundred wholes?"* With your team, find one way to explain how you could figure out how many two fifths are in 100.

7-43. Lee began to wonder how his diagram could help him solve his mother's equation (from problem 7-42). He showed his work below.

$$\frac{2}{5}x = 100$$

$$\frac{5}{2}\left(\frac{2}{5}x\right) = \left(100\right)\frac{5}{2}$$

   a. How does Lee's work relate to the similar-triangles diagram? What is $\frac{5}{2}\left(\frac{2}{5}x\right)$ equal to?

   b. Finish Lee's work to solve for x. Then check your solution.

7-44. Linda and Lee wondered how these new equation-solving strategies would work with different equations. They made up more equations to try to solve. Copy the equations below on your paper and solve each equation using one of the strategies from this lesson. How did you decide which strategy to use?

   a. $\frac{9}{2}x = 27$

   b. $12 = \frac{2}{7}x$

   c. $-\frac{3}{4}x = 21$

METHODS AND MEANINGS

Scaling

When a quantity is increased or decreased by a specific proportion of the original amount, it is changed by a specific scale factor (also called a multiplier). Quantities are **scaled up** when they are increased by multiplying by a number greater than one or **scaled down** when they are decreased by multiplying by a number between (but not including) zero and one.

For example, if a music system is on sale for 25% off its original price of $500, the discount can be found by multiplying by 25%:

$$\text{discount} = 0.25(\text{original price}) = 0.25(\$500) = \$125$$

The full price (100%) minus the discount (25%) would result in the sale price, which in this case is 75% of the original. The sale price can also be found by scaling:

$$\text{sale price} = 0.75(\text{original price}) = 0.75(\$500) = \$375$$

Scaling can be used to enlarge and reduce side lengths of similar shapes, or to increase or decrease times, distances, and other related quantities.

7-45. Mr. Anderson's doctor has advised him to go on a diet. He must reduce his caloric intake by 15%. He currently eats 2800 calories per day. Calculate his new daily caloric intake rate in two different ways, using two different multipliers.

7-46.   Last month, a dwarf lemon tree grew half as much as a semi-dwarf lemon tree. A full-size lemon tree grew three times as much as the semi-dwarf lemon. Together, the three trees grew 27 inches. Write and solve an equation to determine how much each tree grew. Make sure you define your variable.

7-47.   Enrique is saving money to buy a graphing calculator. So far he has saved $30. His math teacher told him he has saved 40% of what he will need. How much does the calculator cost?

7-48.   A principal made the histogram at right to analyze how many years teachers had been teaching at her school.

a.   How many teachers work at her school?

b.   If the principal randomly chose one teacher to represent the school at a conference, what is the probability that the teacher would have been teaching at the school for more than 10 years? Write the probability in two different ways.

c.   What is the probability that a teacher on the staff has been there for fewer than 5 years?

7-49.   Lue is rolling a random number cube. The cube has six sides, and each one is labeled with a different number 1 through 6.

a.   What is the probability that he will roll a 5 or a 3 on one roll?

b.   What is the probability that he will roll a 5 and then a 3 in two rolls?

c.   What is the probability that he will roll a sum of 12 in two rolls?

7-50.   This problem is a checkpoint for simplifying expressions. It will be referred to as Checkpoint 7A.

a. $4x^2 + 3x - 7 + (-2x^2) - 2x + (-3)$ b. $-3x^2 - 2x + 5 + 4x^2 - 7x + 6$

Check your answers by referring to the Checkpoint 7A materials located at the back of your book.

Ideally, at this point you are comfortable working with these types of problems and can solve them correctly. If you feel that you need more confidence when solving these types of problems, then review the Checkpoint 7A materials and try the practice problems provided. From this point on, you will be expected to do problems like these correctly and with confidence.

7.1.5 How can I eliminate the fractions?

Creating Integer Coefficients

Often, one of the best ways to deal with a challenging task is to find a way to make the task easier. For example, lifting a heavy weight can be made easier with a lever or pulley. Mathematical problems are very similar; often, a challenging problem can be changed to create a new problem that is much easier to solve. In this lesson, you will develop strategies for rewriting a complicated equation into an equivalent equation that is more familiar and easier to solve.

7-51.   COMMUNITY SERVICE

The community service club at North Middle School is planning to paint apartments at the local senior citizen center next week. The club needs your help to determine how many apartments they should be able to paint in a day. Earlier in the year, when only $\frac{4}{7}$ of the students worked, they painted 9 apartments in one day. Next week, all of the students are available.

a.   Assume that all of the student workers contribute equally to the work. If x represents the number of apartments that can be painted by all of the students in the club, use a multiplier and your understanding of scaling to represent this situation as an equation.

b.   Choose a strategy to solve your equation in part (a). What does your answer represent? Be ready to share your strategy.

7-52.   HOW CAN I MAKE WHOLES?

Janice, the club's president, began to
think about how she could visualize
$\frac{4}{7}x$ to help her solve her equation
(from problem 7-51). She recalled
using algebra tiles to represent x.
In her mind, she visualized the
diagram at right.

a.   Does this Equation Mat represent your equation from problem 7-51? Why
     or why not?

b.   Janice recognized that these
     numbers were not easy to work
     with, since she did not have whole
     tiles. After working on her paper
     for a while, she said, *"Maybe I
     can make whole tiles using more
     than one set of partial tiles."* She
     drew the diagram shown at right.

     What is her new equation as represented in this picture?

c.   With your team or class, discuss Janice's strategy for solving this equation.
     During your discussion, answer the following questions (in any order):

     •   What made Janice's strategy different than what you did in Lesson
         7.1.4?

     •   How many sets of $\frac{4}{7}x$ did Janice use to get a whole number of
         algebra tiles?

     •   Why did the right-hand side of the equation change?

     •   How does the number of sets Janice used relate to the equation you
         wrote in part (a)?

7-53.   Will the strategy of turning fractions into integers from problem 7-52 work with
         other equations, such as $\frac{2}{3}x = 8$? Consider this question as you answer the
         questions below.

a.   How many sets of $\frac{2}{3}x$ would make a whole number of x-tiles?

b.   Solve for x using Janice's method from problem 7-52. How could you
     record your work on your paper?

c.   Show how your solution is also the number of two thirds in 8 wholes
     (written $8 \div \frac{2}{3}$).

7-54.   Janice wondered if the method of creating whole-
         number x-terms would work with decimals.
         Suppose an item was marked 15% off and the
         sale cost was $36.21. She wrote the equation
         below:

$$0.85x = 36.21$$

a.   Why did she write 0.85 in her equation?

b.   Is there a number she can multiply both sides of the equation by to get an
      integer coefficient (so there is no decimal)? If so, list at least one. If not,
      explain why not.

c.   Use Janice's strategy to solve the equation. What was the original price of
      the item?

d.   Does this method work for all equations with decimal coefficients? What if
      you wanted to solve the equation $1.2x = 14$? What about $0.999x = 71.2$?
      Discuss these equations with your team and write down your conclusion.

7-55.   Solve each equation below by changing the number that x is being multiplied
         by (the coefficient of x) to an integer. Check your answer.

a. $\frac{5}{6}x = 4$ b. $0.8x = 19$

c. $\frac{5}{3}x = 12$ d. $0.12x = 1$

7-56.   LEARNING LOG

         In your Learning Log, summarize at least two strategies
         to solve an equation with fractional (or decimal)
         coefficients. Provide an example for each strategy and
         include a diagram. Title this entry "Solving Equations
         with Fractional Coefficients" and include today's date.

METHODS AND MEANINGS

Box Plots

A **box plot** (sometimes called a "box-and-whisker plot") displays a summary of data using the median, quartiles, and extremes of the data. The box contains "the middle half" of the data. The right segment represents the top 25% of the data, and the left segment represents the bottom 25% of the data. A box plot makes it easy to see where the data are spread out and where they are concentrated. The larger the box, the more the data are spread out.

To construct a box plot using a number line that shows the range of the data, draw vertical line segments above the median, first quartile, and third quartile. Then connect the lines from the first and third quartiles to form a rectangle. Place a vertical line segment above the number line at the highest and lowest data values. Connect the minimum value to the first quartile and the maximum value to the third quartile using horizontal segments. The box plot is shown below for the data set 2, 7, 9, 12, 14, 22, 32, 36, and 43.

7-57.   Erika is tracking the depth of the water in her local creek. Her first twelve measurements are below, in inches:

16 15 13 12 17 14 11 9 11 9 10 9

a.   Find the median, first quartile (Q1), and third quartile (Q3).

b.   Create a box plot for the data. Read the Math Notes box in this lesson to review how to make a box plot.

c.   What is the interquartile range (IQR) for Erika's data?

7-58.   If $\frac{1}{4}$ of x is 16, what is $\frac{3}{4}$ of x? Justify your answer in more than one way.

7-59.   LuAnn talked on her cell phone for 180 minutes, using $\frac{3}{7}$ of her total monthly minutes. Find out how many total minutes LuAnn gets to talk in one month using at least two different methods.

7-60.   Write the inequality represented by each graph.

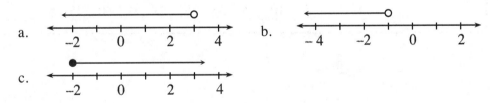

a.

b.

c.

7-61.   *Tires R Us* is having a 30%-off sale. Find the savings on a tire that regularly costs $45.

7-62.   Simplify each expression.

a. $3.3(x+4)$

b. $9-5\frac{1}{2}x-3(-2x+1)$

c. $2.2(3.1+x)+3x$

7.1.6 How can I solve complicated equations?

Creating Integer Coefficients Efficiently

In this lesson, you will continue to develop strategies to rewrite a complicated equation into an equivalent equation that is more familiar and easier to solve.

7-63.   Chari volunteers over the summer in a veterinarian's clinic. The doctor has told Chari to determine the correct dose of medicine to give to the cat, Sweetie, who weighs 9.5 pounds. The dosage (in ml) for a 9.5-pound cat is given by x in the formula below.

$$\frac{2x}{3} + \frac{4}{3} = \frac{10}{3}$$

Chari had never solved such a complicated equation before. She thought about how Janice visualized algebra tiles in problem 7-52 and wondered if that could help. Chari visualized the following diagram.

Help Chari rewrite the equation with integers. Determine the correct dose of medicine to give to Sweetie.

7-64.   Examine the equation below.

$$\frac{x}{4} - \frac{5}{6} = 7$$

a.   Multiply each term by 4. What happened? Do any fractions remain?

b.   If you have not already done so, decide how you can change your result from part (a) so that no fractions remain. Then solve the resulting equation.

c.   Multiplying $\frac{x}{4} - \frac{5}{6} = 7$ by 4 did not eliminate all the fractions. What could you have multiplied by to get rid of all the fractions? Explain how you got your answer and write the equivalent equation that has no fractions.

d.   Solve the resulting equation from part (c) and check your solution in the original equation.

7-65. The method you used in problem 7-64 to eliminate fractions from an equation can be called **Fraction Busters**, because the multiplication of the equation by a common denominator or several of the denominators eliminates, or "busts," the fractions. The result is an equation with no fractions.

Chari is attempting to solve the equation below.

$$\frac{2b}{3} - \frac{1}{6} = \frac{b}{2}$$

a. What is a common denominator for these fractions? Discuss with your team how you could use the common denominator to eliminate the fractions in Chari's equation.

b. If you have not already done so, find an equivalent equation without fractions.

c. Solve for b and check your answer.

7-66. Chari is worried that Sweetie is too thin. The doctor tells Chari that the weight of a typical cat like Sweetie is given by w in the formula below. A healthy cat is within 2 pounds of the typical weight. Is Sweetie too thin?

$$\frac{3w}{10} + \frac{w}{5} = 5.5$$

7-67. Work with your team to solve the following equations. Can you find a number to multiply by that will eliminate all of the fractions in one step?

a. $\frac{5x}{6} + \frac{11}{4} = \frac{17}{3}$ b. $\frac{x}{6} = \frac{1}{12} + \frac{x}{8}$ c. $\frac{x}{3} - \frac{2}{5} = \frac{4}{15} + \frac{2x}{9}$

7-68. Use Fraction Busters in reverse to rewrite the equations below with smaller integer coefficients to make them easier to solve. Solve each equation and check your solution.

a. $300x - 1500 = 2400$ b. $36 - 3r = 18 - 6r$

7-69. Rewrite the equations below to make them easier to solve. Solve each equation and check your solution.

a. $0.04x + 0.16 = 0.06 + 0.08x$ b. $4r^2 + 48 = 4r + 24 + 4r^2 - 8r$

c. $\frac{33}{2} + \frac{3y}{5} = \frac{7y}{10} + 15$ d. $\frac{4}{x} + 11 = \frac{35}{3}$

METHODS AND MEANINGS

MATH NOTES

Solving Equations with Algebraic Fractions (also known as Fraction Busters)

Example: Solve $\frac{x}{3} + \frac{x}{5} = 2$ for x.

$$\frac{x}{3} + \frac{x}{5} = 2$$

This equation would be much easier to solve if it had no fractions. Therefore, the first goal is to find an equivalent equation that has no fractions.

The lowest common denominator of $\frac{x}{3}$ and $\frac{x}{5}$ is 15.

$$15 \cdot \left(\frac{x}{3} + \frac{x}{5}\right) = 15 \cdot 2$$

To eliminate the denominators, multiply all of the terms on both sides of the equation by the common denominator. In this example, the lowest common denominator is 15, so multiplying all of the terms (both sides) in the equation by 15 eliminates the fractions. Another approach is to multiply all of the terms in the equation by one denominator and then by the other. Either way, the result is an equivalent equation without fractions.

$$15 \cdot \frac{x}{3} + 15 \cdot \frac{x}{5} = 15 \cdot 2$$

$$5x + 3x = 30$$
$$8x = 30$$

$$x = \frac{30}{8} = \frac{15}{4} = 3.75$$

In this course, the number used to eliminate the denominators is called a **Fraction Buster**. Now the equation looks like many you have seen before, and it can be solved in the usual way.

Check: $\frac{3.75}{3} + \frac{3.75}{5} = 2$

$$1.25 + 0.75 = 2 \checkmark$$

Once you have found the solution, remember to check your answer.

7-70. Use the Fraction Busters to solve the following problems.

    a. $\frac{3}{2} + \frac{2x}{5} = \frac{7}{10}$
               b. $\frac{-8x}{5} + \frac{1}{6} = \frac{-5x}{3}$

7-71. Find the value of x that makes each equation true.

    a. $-4.9x = 9.8$
        b. $\frac{8}{21} = -\frac{2}{7}x$
        c. $\frac{3}{5} + x = \frac{2}{3}$

Core Connections, Course 2

7-72. Trina planted 43 plants in her garden last week. She planted twice as many cucumbers as zucchini and eight more tomatoes than cucumbers. Write and solve an equation to find the number of each kind of plant in her garden. If you need to, use the 5-D Process to help you organize your thinking. Be sure to define your variable.

7-73. Complete the scaling for each number line below.

a.

b.

c.

d.

7-74. Mt. Rose Middle School collected canned food to donate to a local charity. Each classroom kept track of how many cans it collected. The number of cans in each room were 107, 55, 39, 79, 86, 62, 65, 70, 80, and 77. The principal displayed the data in the box plot below.

a. What is the interquartile range of the data?

b. The main office staff collected 55 cans, the counseling staff collected 89 cans, and the custodial staff collected 67 cans.

On grid paper, make a new box plot that includes this data. Clearly label the median and the first and third quartiles.

7-75. Ages of golfers participating in a golf tournament were 44, 48, 40, 25, 28, 37, 29, 34, 45, 51, 43, 35, 38, 57, 50, 35, 47, 30, 61, 43, 44, 60, 46, 43, 33, 45, 42, 34, 32, and 74.

a. Create a stem-and-leaf plot for this data.

b. Use the stem-and-leaf plot to create a histogram.

c. Describe the shape and spread of the data. Are there any apparent outliers?

d. Use the appropriate measure of center to describe the "typical" age of golfers at the tournament.

7.1.7 Percent of what?

Percent Increase and Decrease

Perhaps you have heard an adult say something like, *"When I was growing up, it only cost a dime to go to the movies!"* The rate at which prices increase over a period of time, called **inflation**, is one of the many things that mathematics can help you understand. In this lesson, you will be using diagrams and computations to calculate the way quantities (like cost or height) change.

As you work today, keep the following questions in mind.

Is it increasing or decreasing?

What is it changing from?

By how much did it change?

7-76. **WHAT IS THE PERCENT INCREASE?**

Several years ago, Joe started a lawn-care business. Due to rising costs, he needs to increase his prices. He is concerned, however, because he has heard that if he raises his rates more than 33%, he might lose business. At right is a letter he sent to his clients.

Joe began to wonder about how the increase in his fees could be expressed in terms of a percent.

> *Dear Valued Customer,*
>
> *After several years of business, Mowcare is increasing its price for lawn service. Since the cost of gas and other supplies has increased, we need to raise our prices. Our prices will increase from $12.50 per hour to $15 per hour. We hope you continue to be happy with the quality of our work.*
>
> *Sincerely,*
> *Joe*

a. Joe wants to determine the scale factor (multiplier) for the price increase and wrote the following equation:

$$12.50x = 15$$

Explain how this expression represents this situation. What does x represent?

b. Solve the equation above to determine the scale factor for his change in fees. Represent this multiplier (scale factor) as a fraction, as a decimal, and as a percent.

Problem continues on next page. →

7-76.   *Problem continued from previous page.*

    c. How could this situation be represented with a line diagram? With your team, copy and complete the diagram below. Then answer and do the following:

        • Which portion of the diagram corresponds to the original price? Circle and label this part "original."

        • Which portion of the diagram corresponds to the change in price? Circle and label this part "change."

    d. When Joe raised his rates, what was the **percent increase**? That is another way of asking: What percent of the original price did the price change? Should Joe expect to lose business?

7-77.   Paige needs your help! She wants to convince her grandmother to let her sign up for a rock-climbing class. The class normally costs $50, but the school is offering a special price of $34. Paige's grandmother wants to know what percent of the cost of the class she would save.

    a. Without calculating, estimate the percent of the discount.

    b. With your team, determine the percent change in the price of the class. Use the prompts below to help guide your team's discussion.

        • Draw a diagram or write an equation that represents the situation.

        • What is the original (whole) value? Indicate this on your diagram or in your equation.

        • What percent is the change? Find and indicate this on your diagram or in your equation.

        • Does this situation represent an increase or decrease?

7-78.   The **percent change** is a comparison of the amount of change to the original amount. If a number increases from the original amount, it is called **percent increase**. If the number decreases from the original, it is called a **percent decrease**.

a.   What is the percent change from $30 to $33? Is this a percent increase or decrease? To answer this question:

- Draw a diagram to represent the problem.

- Determine if it is a percent increase or decrease.

- Calculate the percent change.

b.   What is the percent change from $33 to $30? Is this a percent increase or decrease? To answer this question:

- Draw a diagram to represent the problem.

- Determine if it is a percent increase or decrease.

- Calculate the percent change.

c.   If both parts (a) and (b) above have a change of $3, why are the percent changes different? Explain.

7-79.   To attract new customers, a shoe company called Shoe Fits will raise its prices 10% and then offer a 10%-off coupon.

a.   Without doing any calculations, consider the following question: If a coupon is used, do you think the final price will be more than, less than, or the same as the original price? Discuss this with your team and be ready to share your thinking with the class.

b.   Akari wants to use a coupon to buy a pair of shoes that originally cost $46. What will the increased price be? What will be the price after the 10%-off coupon is used? Show all calculations. Does this result confirm your answer to part (a)?

c.   Akari had assumed that if the price increased 10% and then he received a 10% discount, it would return to the original price. Explain why this did not happen.

Core Connections, Course 2

METHODS AND MEANINGS

Percent Increase or Decrease

A **percent increase** is the amount that a quantity has increased, represented as a percent of the original amount. A **percent decrease** is the amount that a quantity has decreased, written as a percent of the original amount. You can write an equation to represent a percent change that is an increase or decrease using a scale factor or multiplier:

amount of increase or decrease = (% change)(original amount)

Example 1: A loaf of bread increased in price from $0.29 to $2.89 in the past 50 years. What was the percent increase?

increase = $2.89 − $0.29
= $2.60

$2.60 = (x)($0.29)

$\frac{\$2.60}{\$0.29} = x$

$x \approx 8.97$ or 897%

Example 2: Calculator prices decreased from $59 to $9.95. What was the percent decrease?

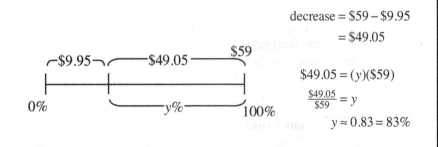

decrease = $59 − $9.95
= $49.05

$49.05 = (y)($59)

$\frac{\$49.05}{\$59} = y$

$y \approx 0.83 = 83\%$

7-80. Joe wanted to know more about how the cost of fertilizer for his lawn-care business was changing. The cost of a bag of fertilizer just increased from $8 to $15. What is the percent increase of the price? Represent the change as a fraction, as a percent, and as a decimal.

7-81. Solve each equation. Show all work.

    a. $0.85x = 200$
                       b. $\frac{7}{6}x = 140$

7-82. Ms. Poppy has finished grading her students' tests. The scores were $62, 65, 93, 51, 55, 76, 79, 85, 55, 72, 78, 83, 91$, and 82.

    a. Find the median.
                            b. Find the quartiles.

    c. Find the IQR.
                              d. Find the mean.

7-83. Mr. Crow, the head groundskeeper at High Tech Middle School, mows the lawn along the side of the gym. The lawn is rectangular, and the length is 5 feet more than twice the width. The perimeter of the lawn is 250 feet.

    a. Use the 5-D Process to find the dimensions of the lawn.

    b. Use the dimensions you calculated in part (a) to find the area of the lawn.

7-84. Evaluate the inequality below for the following listed values of x. Decide if the value makes the statement true or false. Show your work.

$$3x - 3 \geq 2x + 3$$

    a. $x = -3$
           b. $x = 9.5$
           c. $x = 6$
           d. $x = 10\frac{1}{2}$

7-85. Mr. Takaya can eat three slices of pizza in five minutes. If he continues to eat at the same rate, how long will it take him to eat the whole pizza, which has twelve slices? How many slices could he eat in half of an hour?

7.1.8 How does it change over time?

Simple Interest

When banks lend money, they charge **interest**, which is a fee for letting the borrower use the money. Interest is usually expressed as a percent of the amount borrowed and is added to the amount that the borrower owes. For example, a bank might charge someone an 8% annual (yearly) interest rate for borrowing $500. In addition, if you have money in a savings account, banks generally pay interest to you on the money in the account. So by leaving your money in a bank, you can earn more money.

There are different ways of calculating interest, and each one creates different patterns of growth. As you work with your team to investigate one kind of interest called **simple interest**, ask these questions to focus your discussion:

What patterns do you see?

How can you show the connection?

7-86.   RENTING THE HALL

The student council is planning a spring celebration. Unfortunately, to rent a hall for the event, they will need to pay a deposit in advance of the event. Since they have not started selling tickets yet, they asked the Parent-Teacher Association for a loan of $825 for the hall rental. The PTA agreed, but said it would charge 2% simple interest each week until the loan is paid back.

Ms. Becker, the student-council advisor, explained to the students that the amount of the loan ($825) is called the **principal** amount. Until the loan is paid back, 2% (called the weekly **interest rate**) of the principal amount will be added each week to the amount owed.

a.   How much money in interest will the PTA charge each week?

b.   If the student council borrows $825, how much will it owe after 1 week? After 3 weeks? Show your calculations.

c.   How much would the student council owe two months (8 weeks) from now? Be prepared to justify your strategy.

7-87.   The student-council members realized that they would also need funds before the event to pay the DJ and photographer a deposit. They will need a second loan of $1000 to pay for these two expenses.

    a.   If the PTA also charges them 2% weekly simple interest for this loan, how much will be added to this loan each week?

    b.   The PTA has decided that to cover its costs, it only needs to earn $18 interest each week. What percent weekly interest should the PTA charge the student council for this loan? Be prepared to share your strategy.

7-88.   A loan agreement between the student council and the PTA has finally been reached, but the PTA will not loan the full $1825 requested. To make sure everyone understands the agreement, the PTA created the table below.

Number of Weeks	Calculations	Total Loan Amount
0	$1250	$1250
1	$1250 + $18.75	$1268.75
2	$1250 + $18.75 + $18.75	$1287.50
3		
4		

    a.   Based on this table, how much will the student council borrow? What is the percent interest?

    b.   How much will the student council owe after 3 weeks? After 4 weeks? Show your calculations.

    c.   How is the amount of money that the student council owes changing each week? Show how this change can be found in your table.

    d.   The student-council president wants to be able to check quickly how much the student council owes at any point. Use your table to write a variable expression that shows the amount of money the club owes the PTA after any number of weeks. Make sure to define your variable.

    e.   The president figured out that if the student council does not pay off the loan by the end of the school year, it would owe $1500. How many weeks of school are left? Use your expression from part (d) to write and solve an equation to answer this question.

7-89.   SHOPPING AROUND

The treasurer of the student council decided to look into other funding options for the DJ and the photographer. With your team, examine how each loan would grow and find a way to compare the loans. Assume that a month is 4 weeks. Then find answers to the questions below.

The local bank offered to loan the student council $955 for 1% weekly simple interest.	The Math Club offered to loan the student council $940 for 4.5% monthly simple interest.	The Booster Club offered to loan the student council $960 and would add $36 interest each month.

a.   Which loan would grow most quickly? That is, which has the most interest added each month?

b.   What is the monthly interest rate the Booster Club is offering? Show how you got your answer.

c.   For which loan would the student council owe the most money overall after 3 months? Justify your answer.

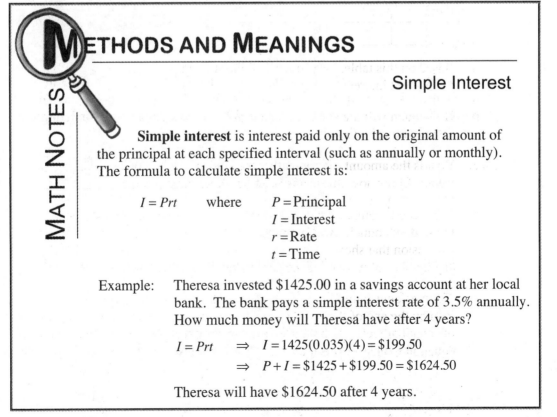

METHODS AND MEANINGS

Simple Interest

MATH NOTES

Simple interest is interest paid only on the original amount of the principal at each specified interval (such as annually or monthly). The formula to calculate simple interest is:

$$I = Prt \quad \text{where} \quad \begin{aligned} P &= \text{Principal} \\ I &= \text{Interest} \\ r &= \text{Rate} \\ t &= \text{Time} \end{aligned}$$

Example: Theresa invested $1425.00 in a savings account at her local bank. The bank pays a simple interest rate of 3.5% annually. How much money will Theresa have after 4 years?

$$I = Prt \quad \Rightarrow \quad I = 1425(0.035)(4) = \$199.50$$
$$\Rightarrow \quad P + I = \$1425 + \$199.50 = \$1624.50$$

Theresa will have $1624.50 after 4 years.

7-90.   Ida wants to buy a car, but she currently does not have any money. The car she wants costs $2500. Consider her two options and decide which loan she should take.

a.   She could borrow $2500 at a monthly interest rate of 4% simple interest and pay the total after 12 months. Write a simple-interest expression and calculate what she would owe at the end of 12 months.

b.   She could borrow $2500 at a weekly interest rate of 1% simple interest and pay the total after 12 months. Show calculations and a written explanation to justify your answer.

7-91.   The Jones family wants to remodel their kitchen. They have saved $23,000 in the last two years. Their contractor says the remodel will cost $40,000. They can borrow the difference at a monthly interest rate of 2% simple interest. If they pay the loan off in six months, how much will they have paid?

7-92.   The electronics department is having a No Sales Tax Sale! In addition, all of the items in the department are on sale for 25% off. Wyatt is looking at a music player that normally costs $120. He has $95 to spend, and he is wondering if he has enough money to buy it.

a.   Wyatt sketched the diagram at right. Use the work he started to find 25% of $120. Is this the price he will pay?

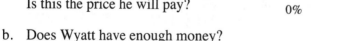

b.   Does Wyatt have enough money?

c.   Would he have enough money if he had to pay the 5.5% sales tax on the sale price?

7-93.   For each equation below, solve for x. Show the process you use to check your answer.

a. $x - \frac{2}{5} = 1\frac{3}{5}$ b. $5x = 0$ c. $x - 14.6 = 2.96$

7-94.　Marty is saving money to buy a new computer. He received $200 for his birthday and saves $150 of each week's paycheck.

Does this situation represent a proportional relationship? If it does, identify the constant of proportionality. If it does not, explain why not.

7-95.　Elvin found the box plot below in the school newspaper.

Number of hours spent watching TV each week

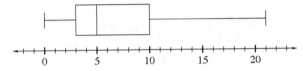

a. Based on the plot, what percent of students watch more than 10 hours of television each week?

b. Based on the plot, what percent of students watch less than 5 hours of television each week?

c. Can Elvin use the plot to find the mean (average) number of hours of television students watch each week? If so, what is it? Explain your reasoning.

d. Can he use the plot to find the median? If so, what is it? Explain your reasoning.

7.2.1 What is the missing number?

Finding Missing Information in Proportional Relationships

Throughout this course, you have made connections between different representations of proportional relationships. In this lesson, all of these ideas will come together to uncover a new strategy for finding missing quantities in proportional relationships.

7-96. In Chapter 4, Kaci was trying to figure out how many pounds of Havarti cheese she could buy for $10, knowing that 3 pounds costs $7.50. She wrote the equivalent ratios below.

$$\frac{3 \text{ pounds}}{\$7.50} = \frac{x}{\$10}$$

Work with your team to brainstorm a list of all of the methods that you can think of that Kaci could use to find the information she is missing. Be prepared to share your ideas with the rest of the class.

7-97. Graeme knows that he earns $4.23 every half hour. He wanted to know how much money he would earn after one full week of work (40 hours). He wrote the equivalent ratios below and quickly sees a way to find his answer.

$$\frac{\$4.23}{\frac{1}{2} \text{ hour}} = \frac{x}{40 \text{ hours}}$$

a. What do you think Graeme is thinking of doing?

b. Solve Graeme's equation.

c. Graeme wants to know how long it will take him to earn $1000. Write and solve an equation to help him figure it out.

7-98.   Shiloh knows that it takes 5 cups of flour to make 2 recipes of cookies. He has 13 cups of flour left in his cupboard. He wants to know how many recipes he can make. He wrote the equivalent ratios below.

$$\frac{5 \text{ cups}}{2 \text{ recipes}} = \frac{13 \text{ cups}}{x \text{ recipes}}$$

This equation looked difficult to solve, so he decided to ask his friend Carolyn for help. Carolyn said,

"If it takes 5 cups of flour to make 2 recipes, then it takes $2\frac{1}{2}$ cups of flour for each recipe. This is the multiplier. Can't you just use the multiplier to write an equation?"

Carolyn then wrote the equation $F = 2\frac{1}{2}R$ where F stands for cups of flour and R stands for the number of recipes. As Carolyn wrote the equation below, she said, *"Then I would solve this equation to find out the number of recipes."*

$$13 = 2\frac{1}{2}R$$

a.   Compare Shiloh and Carolyn's equations. Are they correct? Why or why not?

b.   Which equation is easiest to solve? Solve it.

c.   Does your solution work in both Shiloh and Carolyn's equations?

7-99.   Find the missing information in each set of equivalent ratios below, using any method. Be sure that you record your process so that others can see what you did.

a. $\frac{2}{15} = \frac{x}{5}$

b. $\frac{x}{100} = \frac{7}{8}$

c. $\frac{0.2}{2} = \frac{1}{x}$

d. $\frac{y}{11.2} = \frac{4}{7}$

7-100.   Find the missing value in each of the pairs of equivalent ratios below.

a. $\frac{x}{10} = \frac{6}{15}$ b. $\frac{12}{9} = \frac{8}{x}$ c. $\frac{16}{38} = \frac{200}{m}$

7-101.   Samantha's parents are going to paint her room. Her color choices for the walls include three different shades of white, four shades of tan, two shades of blue, three shades of green, and four shades of pink. What is the probability that she will randomly select any shade of blue or pink?

7-102.   The local sports shop has backpacks on sale for $28. The original price was $40. What is the percent decrease for the backpack price?

7-103.   Simplify the expressions below.

a. $\frac{3}{4} - \frac{1}{3} + (-\frac{5}{24})$ b. $\frac{10}{12} \div \frac{1}{4}$ c. $3\frac{1}{2} \cdot 1\frac{3}{8}$

d. $-\frac{20}{7} \div \frac{1}{3}$ e. $-\frac{8}{25} \cdot (-\frac{15}{32})$ f. $\frac{9}{4} \div (-\frac{2}{3})$

g. $\frac{8}{21} + (-\frac{3}{7})$ h. $\frac{7}{4} \cdot (-\frac{2}{5}) \cdot \frac{3}{5}$

7-104.   Stephanie is earning simple interest of 3.5% on her money each month. She currently has $1325 in her account. What will her balance be in 5 months?

7-105.   Eduardo's friends guessed how many jelly beans were in a jar at his birthday party. Here are their guesses: 75, 80, 95, 92, 100, 72, 71, 60, 65, 88, 60, 152.

a.   Make a histogram to display the data.

b.   Make a box plot to display the data.

c.   Which measure of center is most appropriate for this data? Why?

d.   Which data display most clearly shows the median of the data?

Core Connections, Course 2

7.2.2 How can I find the missing value?

Solving Proportions

You have examined several proportional situations (such as the price of yogurt versus the number of pounds of yogurt) and non-proportional situations (such as the value of a college fund over time). Today you will continue to develop strategies for solving proportional equations.

7-106. J.R. reduced figure A at right to create similar figure B.

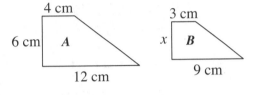

a. Write all of the ratios that compare the corresponding sides of figure B to figure A. What is the relationship between these ratios? How do you know?

b. One of the relationships between the sides can be written as $\frac{3}{4} = \frac{x}{6}$. Find two different ways to find the value of x in this equation. Is your answer reasonable? Be ready to share your strategies with the class.

7-107. MULTIPLE STRATEGIES

J.R.'s team is trying to find multiple ways to solve $\frac{3}{4} = \frac{x}{6}$ from problem 7-106. With your team, analyze each of the strategies below. Some of these strategies might be the same as what you came up with in problem 7-106. However, others may be new. Work to understand each strategy so that you can use it to solve a new problem.

a. J.R. wants to use a **Giant One** to help find the value of x. Explain how he can find a value to use as a numerator and denominator in a Giant One, then find the value of x.

$$\frac{3}{4} \cdot \boxed{1} = \frac{x}{6}$$

Problem continues on next page. →

7-107.   *Problem continued from previous page.*

   b.   Looking at J.R.'s work, Leticia said, *"I see it differently. We just need to find some number that when divided by 6 you get $\frac{3}{4}$. We can undo the division by multiplying each side of the proportion by 6 like this."* Then Leticia showed J.R. the work below.

$$\left(\frac{6}{1}\right)\frac{3}{4} = \frac{x}{6}\left(\frac{6}{1}\right)$$

   With your team, explain how Leticia's idea works. Are the two ratios still equal? Why did she choose to multiply by 6? Simplify each side of the equation.

   c.   Avner asked, *"But if multiplying both sides by 6 gets rid of the denominator of the x, then can we use the same strategy to get rid of the 4 in the other denominator? Like when we do Fraction Busters, right?"* Discuss Avner's question and decide if undoing both denominators using a Fraction Buster is a reasonable strategy. Does this help solve the equation?

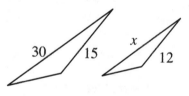

Avner's work

7-108.   Use the strategies from problem 7-107 to solve the problems below.

   a.   Use Leticia's method of undoing division to solve this proportion: $\frac{p}{22.5} = \frac{7}{5}$. When you find p, replace the value in the original proportion to confirm that the two ratios are equal.

   b.   Write and solve a proportional equation for x for the similar triangles at right. Then use Avner's method of undoing both denominators (Fraction Busters) to solve for x.

   c.   An apple-juice container has a tiny hole in it, so it is slowly leaking. If the container leaks three ounces every 19 minutes, how long will it take for the 16 ounces of juice in the container to leak out? Write a proportional equation and solve with J.R.'s strategy of using a Giant One.

7-109.   For each problem below, decide if the situation is proportional. If the problem is proportional, say so, and then solve the problem using any strategy you choose. If the problem is not proportional, explain why not, and then solve the problem.

a.   Steve drove 130 miles from Portland to Tacoma in 2 hours. If he continues to drive at the same speed, how long will it take him to drive 390 miles?

b.   At an amusement park, you pay a $15 entrance fee and then $4 for each ride you go on. How much will it cost you to go on seven rides?

c.   Armando has collected 39 bottle caps in the past three months. At this rate, how many bottle caps will he have in five months?

d.   The grocery store sells 3 limes for 99 cents. At this rate, how much will a dozen limes cost?

e.   Margarit drove her friends to a movie. She drove for 30 minutes at 10 miles per hour in heavy traffic, and then she drove for 15 minutes at 40 miles per hour. How far did she travel in those 45 minutes?

7-110.   After Ramona had solved several proportional equations, she noticed a pattern. *"When we eliminated both of the fractions by multiplying by both denominators, we ended up with something that looks like we just multiplied diagonally."*

$$\frac{10}{4} = \frac{x}{7}$$
$$(7)(10) = (x)(4)$$

a.   What does she mean? For each of the proportions below, apply Ramona's diagonal multiplying pattern and determine whether the result is a true mathematical equation. Will her pattern always work?

   i. $\frac{8}{10} = \frac{12}{15}$ ii. $\frac{6}{4} = \frac{9}{6}$ iii. $\frac{15}{3} = \frac{20}{4}$

b.   Use Ramona's pattern to solve the equation $\frac{2}{5} = \frac{11}{x}$ for x.

7-111.   LEARNING LOG

In this section, you have used a number of different strategies for finding missing information in proportional relationships.

In your Learning Log, show each of these methods. Include examples to show your thinking. Title this entry "Methods for Finding Missing Information in Proportional Relationships" and label it with today's date.

Solving Proportions

An equation stating that two ratios are equal is called a **proportion**. Some examples of proportions are shown at right.

$$\frac{6 \text{ mi}}{2 \text{ hr}} = \frac{9 \text{ mi}}{3 \text{ hr}}$$

$$\frac{5}{7} = \frac{50}{70}$$

When two ratios are known to be equal, setting up a proportion is one strategy for solving for an unknown part of one ratio. For example, if the ratios $\frac{9}{2}$ and $\frac{x}{16}$ are equal, setting up the proportion $\frac{x}{16} = \frac{9}{2}$ allows you to solve for x.

Strategy 1: One way to solve this proportion is by using a **Giant One** to find the equivalent ratio. In this case, since 2 times 8 is 16, so use $\frac{8}{8}$ for the Giant One.

$$\frac{x}{16} = \frac{9}{2} \cdot \boxed{\frac{8}{8}} \quad \text{and} \quad \frac{9 \cdot 8}{2 \cdot 8} = \frac{72}{16}, \text{ which shows that } \frac{x}{16} = \frac{72}{16}, \text{ so } x = 72.$$

Strategy 2: Undoing division. Another way to solve the proportion is to think of the ratio $\frac{x}{16}$ as, " x divided by 16." To solve for x, use the inverse operation of division, which is multiplication. Multiplying both sides of the proportional equation by 16 "undoes" the division.

$$\frac{x}{16} = \frac{9}{2}$$
$$\left(\frac{16}{1}\right)\frac{x}{16} = \frac{9}{2}\left(\frac{16}{1}\right)$$
$$x = \frac{144}{2} = 72$$

Strategy 3: Use cross multiplication. This is a solving strategy for proportions that is based on the process of multiplying each side of the equation by the denominators of each ratio and setting the two sides equal. It is a shortcut for using a **Fraction Buster** (multiplying each side of the equation by the denominators).

Complete Algebraic Solution (Fraction Busters)	Cross Multiplication
$\dfrac{x}{16} = \dfrac{9}{2}$	$\dfrac{x}{16} = \dfrac{9}{2}$
$2 \cdot 16 \cdot \frac{x}{16} = \frac{9}{2} \cdot 2 \cdot 16$	$\frac{x}{16} \diagdown\!\!\!\!\diagup \frac{9}{2}$
$2 \cdot x = 9 \cdot 16$	$2 \cdot x = 9 \cdot 16$
$2x = 144$	$2x = 144$
$x = 72$	$x = 72$

7-112. Solve the proportions using any strategy you choose. Show all of your steps.

a. $\frac{35}{70} = \frac{x}{100}$

b. $\frac{12}{33} = \frac{m}{11}$

c. $\frac{x}{15} = \frac{12}{75}$

d. $\frac{4}{32} = \frac{10.5}{x}$

7-113. Triangle ABC is similar to triangle DEF.

a. Find the scale factor from triangle ABC to triangle DEF.

b. Find x.

c. Find y.

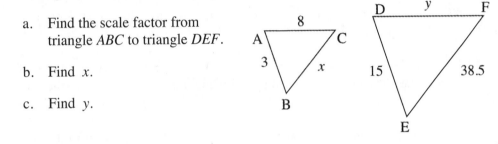

7-114. Write an equation to represent the situation below and answer the question. You may use the 5-D Process to help you.

Andrew just opened a new office-supply store. He has been keeping track of how many customers visit his store. During his second week, he had 18 more customers than he did the first week. The third week, he had four less than twice as many customers as he had during the second week. In his fourth week of business, he had 92 customers. If he had 382 customers in total during his first four weeks of business, how many customers did he have during the second week?

7-115. For each equation below, solve for x. Sometimes the easiest strategy is to use mental math.

a. $x - \frac{3}{5} = 1\frac{2}{5}$

b. $5.2 + x = 10.95$

c. $2x - 3.25 = 7.15$

d. $\frac{x}{16} = \frac{3}{8}$

7-116.   Jessica wants to make a spinner that has all of the following characteristics. Sketch a possible spinner for Jessica. Be sure to label each section of the spinner with a name and with its theoretical probability.

- Blue, red, purple, and green are the only colors on the spinner.

- It is half as likely to land on blue as to land on red.

- It is three times as likely to land on purple as green.

- There is a 50% probability of landing on either blue or red and a 50% probability of landing on either purple or green.

7-117.   This problem is a checkpoint for displays of data. It will be referred to as Checkpoint 7B.

For the information in parts (a) and (b), create a histogram. For the information in parts (c) and (d), create a box plot and then identify the quartiles and interquartile range.

a.   Hours spent doing after school sports each weekday by students:
$0, 4, 0, 1, 1, 1, \frac{1}{2}, 1\frac{1}{2}, 2, 2, \frac{1}{2}, 2, 2, 2, 1\frac{1}{2}, 1\frac{1}{2}, 1, 1, 2, 4, \frac{1}{2}, \frac{1}{2}, 2$

b.   Amount of time spent solving a math puzzle (minutes) by study teams:
$3, 15, 18, 14, 10, 14, 19, 8, 14, 14, 15, 19, 9$

c.   Average number of text messages sent per day by a group of friends:
$47, 52, 50, 47, 51, 46, 49, 46, 48$

d.   Number of points scored by the basketball team during a season:
$76, 90, 75, 72, 93, 82, 70, 85, 80$

Check your answers by referring to the Checkpoint 7B materials located at the back of your book.

Ideally, at this point you are comfortable working with these types of problems and can solve them correctly. If you feel that you need more confidence when solving these types of problems, then review the Checkpoint 7B materials and try the practice problems provided. From this point on, you will be expected to do problems like these correctly and with confidence.

Chapter 7 Closure   What have I learned?

Reflection and Synthesis

The activities below offer you a chance to reflect
about what you have learned during this chapter.
As you work, look for concepts that you feel very
comfortable with, ideas that you would like to learn
more about, and topics you need more help with.

①   SUMMARIZING MY UNDERSTANDING

This section gives you an opportunity to show what you know the main math
ideas in this chapter.

With a partner, obtain an envelope from your teacher. Follow the directions
below to demonstrate your understanding of solving equations with rate,
including those with fractional coefficients.

Part 1:   Decide which one of you is going to work a problem and which one
of you is going to listen. (You will do both jobs before you finish
this lesson, so you are just choosing the job you will do first.) The
partner working the problem should draw a problem out of the
envelope.

Part 2:   **If you are working the problem**, clearly show all of your work on
your paper, draw diagrams, and label them completely. Explain what
you are thinking to your partner as you work.

              If you are the listener, pay attention to what your partner is saying
as he or she solves the problem. When your partner is finished, you
must tell him or her whether or not you agree with the solution and
why or why not.

Part 3:   Trade jobs with your partner. The partner now working the problem
should draw a new problem out of the envelope and explain the
solution to the listener.

Two example problems are shown below.

Problem A	Problem F
Omar has been riding his bicycle at a speed of 15 mph for 48 miles. How long has he been riding?	At Maple Middle School, 34% of the students are in seventh grade. If there are 1300 students at the school, how many students are NOT in seventh grade?

WHAT HAVE I LEARNED?

Doing the problems in this section will help you to evaluate which types of problems you feel comfortable with and which ones you need more help with.

Solve each problem as completely as you can. The table at the end of this closure section provides answers to these problems. It also tells you where you can find additional help and where to find practice problems like them.

CL 7-118.   Aja and Emilie were riding their skateboards. They knew that they could ride 3 miles in 20 minutes. Use your problem-solving strategies to find out how far the girls can ride in 45 minutes.

CL 7-119.   Harley was eating pizza and had already eaten six pieces before his sister, Samantha, got home. Samantha was worried that she was not going to get a fair share of the pizza and wanted to know how many pieces were in the pizza originally. Harley told her, "*I have only eaten $\frac{3}{8}$ of the pizza.*" Help Samantha figure out how many pieces of pizza there were to start with.

CL 7-120.   Marcus has a summer job where he makes $45 a day. Yesterday, his boss told him that he was getting a raise to $63 a day because he was such a hard worker. What is the percent increase in Marcus' salary?

CL 7-121.   Simplify and solve the following equations.

a. $5x + 2 = -3x - 14$ b. $\frac{2}{3}x + 1 = x - 4$

c. $0.5x - 0.5 = 0.75x + 1 - x$ d. $5x + 6 - 2x = 3x - 7$

CL 7-122.   Joe is using his allowance money to download songs from the Internet. He can download them at a rate of eight songs every 10 minutes. Jasmine, who is downloading songs with the money she made from her part-time job, can download at a rate of 12 songs every 15 minutes. Who is downloading songs faster?

CL 7-123.   Solve the inequality $8 + x \le 3$ and graph the solutions on a number line.

Core Connections, Course 2

CL 7-124. A biologist was sitting near a pond and noticed a large number of dragonflies. He also saw both frogs and fish trying to eat the dragonflies. He counted a total of 89 fish, frogs, and dragonflies. He noticed that there were four times as many dragonflies as fish and that the frogs were five more than twice the number of fish.

Use the 5-D Process to determine how many fish, frogs, and dragonflies the biologist counted.

CL 7-125. Find the probability of each of the following events. Show all of your work.

a. Flipping a penny and getting a "heads" and then flipping a nickel and getting a "tails."

b. Rolling a 5 on a standard number cube and picking a 10 or a jack from a standard deck of playing cards.

CL 7-126. For each of the problems above, do the following:

- Draw a bar or number line that represents 0 to 10.

- Color or shade in a portion of the bar that represents your level of understanding and comfort with completing that problem on your own.

If any of your bars are less than a 5, choose *one* of those problems and do one of the following tasks:

- Write two questions that you would like to ask about that problem.
- Brainstorm two things that you DO know about that type of problem.

If all of your bars are a 5 or above, choose one of those problems and do one of these tasks:

- Write two questions you might ask or hints you might give to a student who was stuck on the problem.
- Make a new problem that is similar and more challenging than that problem and solve it.

WHAT TOOLS CAN I USE?

You have several tools and references available to help support your learning: your teacher, your study team, your math book, and your Toolkit, to name only a few. At the end of each chapter, you will have an opportunity to review your Toolkit for completeness. You will also revise or update it to reflect your current understanding of big ideas.

The main elements of your Toolkit should be your Learning Logs, Math Notes, and the vocabulary used in this chapter. Math words that are new appear in bold in the text. Refer to the lists provided below and follow your teacher's instructions to revise your Toolkit, which will help make it useful for you as you complete this chapter and as you work in future chapters.

Learning Log Entries

- Lesson 7.1.3 – Scaling Quantities
- Lesson 7.1.5 – Solving Equations with Fractional Coefficients
- Lesson 7.2.2 – Methods for Finding Missing Information in Proportional Relationships

Math Notes

- Lesson 7.1.1 – Histograms and Stem-and-Leaf Plots
- Lesson 7.1.2 – Quantities and Interquartile Range (IQR)
- Lesson 7.1.3 – Describing Data Distributions
- Lesson 7.1.4 – Scaling
- Lesson 7.1.5 – Box Plots
- Lesson 7.1.6 – Solving Equations with Algebraic Fractions (also known as Fraction Busters)
- Lesson 7.1.7 – Percent Increase or Decrease
- Lesson 7.1.8 – Simple Interest
- Lesson 7.2.2 – Solving Proportions

Mathematical Vocabulary

The following is a list of vocabulary found in this chapter. Some of the words have been seen in the previous chapter. The words in bold are words that are new to this chapter. Make sure that you are familiar with the terms below and know what they mean. For the words you do not know, refer to the glossary or index. You might also add these words to your Toolkit so that you can reference them in the future.

box plot	coefficient	constant of proportionality
Fraction Busters	**first quartile**	**Giant One**
histogram	**interest**	**interquartile range (IQR)**
mean	median	measure of central tendency
outlier	**principal**	**percent change**
proportional	rate	scale
similar	**stem-and-leaf plot**	**third quartile**

Answers and Support for Closure Problems
What Have I Learned?

Note: MN = Math Note, LL = Learning Log

Problem	Solution	Need Help?	More Practice
CL 7-118.	The girls can ride $6\frac{3}{4}$ miles in 45 minutes.	Lessons 7.1.1, 7.1.2, 7.2.1, and 7.2.2 MN: 7.1.4, 7.2.2 LL: 7.1.3, 7.2.2	Problems 7-14, 7-21, 7-59, and 7-85
CL 7-119.	There were 16 pieces in the pizza.	Lessons 7.1.4 and 7.1.5 LL: 7.1.5	Problems 7-47, 7-58, and 7-92
CL 7-120.	Marcus' salary increased by 40%.	Lesson 7.1.7 MN: 7.1.7	Problems 7-76, 7-78, 7-80, and 7-102
CL 7-121.	a. $x = -2$ b. $x = 15$ c. $x = 2$ d. no solution	Lessons 7.1.4, 7.1.5, and 7.1.6 MN: 7.1.6 LL: 7.1.5	Problems 7-44, 7-81, 7-93, and 7-115
CL 7-122.	They are downloading at the same rate.	Lessons 4.2.3 MN: 4.2.4	Problem CL 4-147, CL 5-156, and 7-10
CL 7-123.	$x \le -5$	Section 6.1 MN: 6.1.1, 6.1.4 LL: 6.1.4	Problems CL 6-145, 7-60, and 7-84
CL 7-124.	12 fish, 29 frogs, 48 dragonflies	Section 5.3 MN: 5.3.3 LL: 5.3.4	Problems CL 5-150, 7-83, and 7-114
CL 7-125.	a. $\frac{1}{2} \cdot \frac{1}{2} = \frac{1}{4}$ b. $\frac{1}{6} \cdot \frac{2}{13} = \frac{2}{78} = \frac{1}{39}$	Section 5.2 MN: 5.2.4 and 5.2.5 LL: 5.2.1 and 5.2.5	Problems CL 5-151, CL 6-142, 7-25 7-49, and 7-101

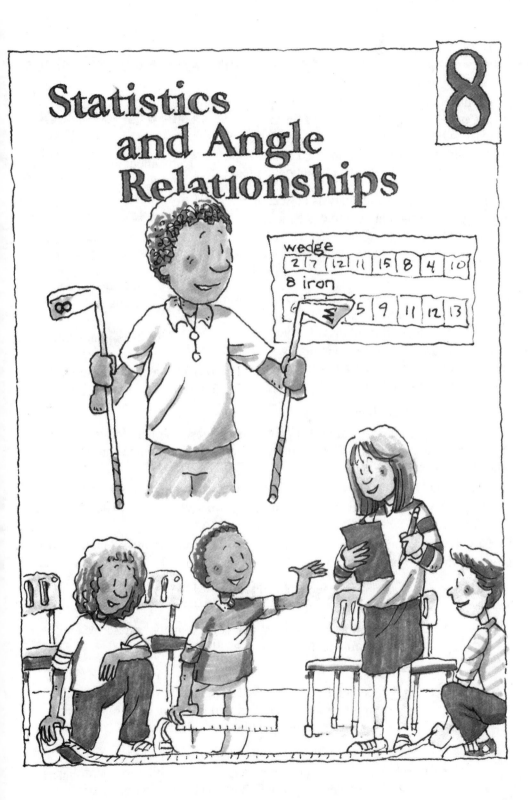

Statistics
and Angle
Relationships

8

wedge

| 2 | 7 | 12 | 11 | | 15 | 8 | 4 | 10 |

8 iron

| | | | | 5 | 9 | 11 | 12 | 13 |

CHAPTER 8   Statistics and Angle Relationships

You may not have noticed, but many homework problems in Chapter 7 helped prepare you for this chapter's work with data. The homework problems equipped you with tools for comparing two sets of data and making inferences about the data based on evidence.

After revisiting data display and analysis in Section 8.1, in Section 8.2 you will look at how to design a good survey. You will learn more about the kinds of questions to ask and the group that you would select to answer them.

In Section 8.3, your focus will shift from statistics toward geometry. You will begin by learning about angles. Specifically, you will learn how to classify them by their sizes and by their relationships to other angles. Then you will build triangles and quadrilaterals with specific characteristics and compare them to each other.

Guiding Questions

Think about these questions throughout this chapter:

How can I describe the data?

How do the data sets compare?

How can I select a good sample?

What can I conclude?

How can I measure it?

In this chapter, you will learn how to:

➢ Describe, analyze and compare sets of data using measures of central tendency, such as mean and median, and using the variation, including range and inter quartile range (IQR).

➢ Attempt to find random and representative samples to complete a survey.

➢ Identify angles by their characteristics and use correct vocabulary to describe and name them.

➢ Construct triangles and quadrilaterals with given side lengths and/or angles and predict if they will be unique shapes.

Chapter Outline

Section 8.1   In this section, you will collect, analyze, describe and compare data.

Section 8.2   In Section 8.2 you will design surveys in order to collect representative data that will help you draw conclusions about the larger population of interest.

Section 8.3   You will build and compare shapes. To compare shapes completely, you will build an angle-measuring device and then use it to investigate angles.

8.1.1 Which tool is more precise?

Measurement Precision

Do the lengths of the object you are measuring or the tool you choose to measure with affect how precise your measurement is likely to be? In this section, your class will explore this question by analyzing the results of an experiment. As you work with your team, think about the questions that follow.

What am I measuring?

What unit is being repeated?

What can I do to make my measurement more precise?

8-1.   WHICH TOOL GIVES A MORE PRECISE MEASUREMENT?

Have you heard the expression, "Measure twice, cut once"? This advice refers to the care that professionals such as carpenters and fashion designers need to take to measure precisely so that all of the parts of their creations fit together correctly. Careful, correct measurements also ensure that they do not waste materials. Does it matter what tool they use to make their measurements?

Imagine using two different tools, such as a 12-inch ruler and a continuous measuring tape, to measure a length of your classroom or the width of a basketball court (in inches). How might the measurements that you get compare?

Discuss the following questions with your team. Be prepared to share your ideas with the rest of the class.

- Would you get the same measurement with each tool?

- Why might the measures be different? Should they be the same?

- Which tool do you think would give you a more precise measurement, that is, one that is closer to the *true* length of the classroom?

8-2.   Now you and your class will gather data to test your ideas about the precision of measuring the same length with two different tools.

Your Task: As directed by your teacher, measure the specified length in the classroom to the nearest inch twice, each time using a different tool (a 12-inch ruler and a single measuring tape, for example). Although you will share tools with your team and work together to make sure the measures are recorded properly, *each person* in the team should measure the length twice, once with each tool.

8-3.   Once your team members have each made their measurements, compare the results within your team by answering the following questions:

- Which tool seems to measure more precisely?

- What do you think is the actual length of the classroom? How did you decide?

- Which tool do you think gave you a better answer?

8-4.   Add your data to the class data table.

a.   Examine the sets of data. Record any initial observations you can make.

b.   Are there any measures that look very different from the others? These extreme values are called **outliers**, because they are far away from most of the data. What could you do to help you see any outliers better?

c.   Sometimes an outlier can reveal that an error or misunderstanding has occurred. Decide as a class if any data needs to be deleted or corrected due to an error or misunderstanding.

d.   What is the range for each set of data? How do the ranges compare? For each set of data, what is the median? What is the first quartile? The third quartile?

8-5.   Creating visual representations of data makes data sets easier to compare.

a.   Make a histogram for each set of data. Make sure to use the same scale for both histograms.

b.   Create box plots for the two sets of data. Put both box plots on the same number line and use the same scale as you did for your histogram.

c.   Compare the center, shape, spread, and outliers for the two sets of data using the histograms and the box plots. Do the data sets seem to show the same value for the length of the classroom?

8-6. WHICH MEASUREMENT IS BEST?

So what is the actual measure? Clearly you have multiple measurements from which to choose. How can you decide what is the best estimate of the length of the classroom?

Look at the data set for each tool, along with their histograms and box plots, and consider the center, shape, spread, and outliers. With your team, discuss what you can learn from each of these pieces of information about the precision (consistency) of each measuring tool, as well as about the length of the classroom. Which of the many numbers that you could choose is the best estimate for the *actual* length of the classroom? Why? What do you think accounts for the greater consistency of one tool?

8-7. IS MEASUREMENT ALWAYS APPROXIMATE?

As you have seen, the measurements that you made are approximate. Is this always true? Can you imagine a way to measure something that would be exact without any variability? Discuss this with your team and be prepared to share your ideas with the class.

8-8. Ms. Whitney has thirteen students who did extra credit assignments to raise their grades. The scores on the assignments were $96, 45, 89, 100, 100, 77, 67, 84, 98, 33, 60, 97,$ and 100.

a. Make a stem-and-leaf plot of this data.

b. Find the median, and the first and third quartiles.

8-9. Simplify each expression.

a. $-\frac{4}{5} + \frac{7}{12}$ b. $\frac{5}{9} + (-\frac{1}{4})$ c. $-\frac{3}{7} \cdot \frac{11}{12}$ d. $-1\frac{2}{3} \cdot \frac{4}{5}$

8-10. Solve the equations below for the variable. Be sure to check your answer.

a. $3(2x - 1) + 2 = 5x$ b. $600x + 200 = 500x$

8-11.   Write an equation to represent this problem and find the unknown side lengths. Use the 5-D Process to help you organize your thinking and to define your variables, if you need to do so. Remember to define your variable.

A trapezoid has a perimeter of 117 cm. The two shortest sides have the same length. The third side is 12 cm longer than one short side. The final side is 9 cm less than three times one short side. How long is each side of the trapezoid?

8-12.   Four pieces of taffy cost 25 cents. Complete the table below.

Taffy (# of pieces)	4	16	8	80	24	32	40
Cost (in dollars)							

8-13.   Mrs. Ferguson, your school librarian, asks you to conduct a survey of how many books students read during the year. You get the following results: 12, 24, 10, 32, 12, 4, 35, 10, 8, 12, 15, 20, 18, 25, 21, and 9.

a.   Use the data to create a histogram. Use a bin width of 10 books. (Remember, if a value falls on the line, place it in the upper bin.)

b.   Is the mean or median a better measure of the center? Find the value of whichever is more appropriate.

c.   Make a box plot of the data.

d.   Describe the center, shape, spread, and outliers of the distribution.

8-14.   Copy and complete each of the Diamond Problems below. The pattern used in the Diamond Problems is shown at right.

a.   b.   c.   d.

8-15.   Solve the following equations using any method. Show your work and check your solution.

a. $5x + 20 = 3x + 4$ b. $7x - 4 = 3x + 8$ c. $2x + 6 = x - 9$

8-16.   Mariana and Felix were in science class and were using a test kit to measure the amount of calcium in milk. They measured the amount of calcium in 1 cup of milk 10 times and got a mean of 294.6 mg. They looked up the amount of calcium that is typically in milk and found out it was 290 mg per 1 cup. Percent error finds the difference between the actual value and measured value and the compares that difference to the actual value as a percentage. Find the percent error of Mariana and Felix's measurement.

8-17.   If five songs can be downloaded for $6, what is the cost of seven songs?

8-18.   Roger has a bag of marbles. There are 6 red, 4 blue, 3 white, and 7 green marbles in the bag. If he draws one marble, replaces it, and then draws another, find the following probabilities. Write your answer as a fraction and a percent.

   a.   P(red, red)

   b.   P(not white, green)

   c.   P(blue or white, red)

   d.   Find the answer for part (a) above if Roger does not replace the marble before selecting the second one.

8.1.2 How can I compare the results?

Comparing Distributions

In Lesson 8.1.1, you compared the results of two different methods of measuring to answer the question, "Which measuring tool is more precise?" Today you will continue to develop your methods for comparing two distributions of data.

8-19.   Josh is just starting a round of golf. This first hole is 130 yards long. He needs to decide which club to use for his first shot. He has kept careful records about how close his first shots came to the hole, all from this same distance. His records include data from his use of two different golf clubs, a wedge and an 8-iron, over the past year.

Wedge, distance to hole (yards): 0 3 1 2 7 2 15 25 5 22
8-iron, distance to hole (yards): 19 12 12 8 3 11 5 7 10 13 8 10 11 20

a.   Create a histogram and box plot for each of the clubs. Place the box plot above the histogram on the same number line for each club to make a combination plot. Use a bin width of 5 yards.

b.   To find the "typical" distance that Josh hits the ball from the hole with a wedge, is the mean or the median a better choice? Find the typical distance Josh hits the ball from the hole with a wedge and compare it to the typical distance he hits the ball with an 8-iron.

c.   Advise Josh which club to use. Explain your thinking.

8-20.   It is just as important to consider the spread of the data as it is to consider the center when comparing data sets.

a.   Calculate the Interquartile Range (IQR) for each golf club in the previous problem. With which club is Josh more consistent?

b.   If Josh decided to use the 8-iron, he could "typically" expect to hit the ball so that it lands between 8 and 12 yards from the hole. This is indicated by the box on the box plot display and corresponds with the IQR. If Josh decided to use the wedge, what is a "typical" interval of distances from the hole he could expect the ball to land?

c.   Compare the typical interval of distances for the 8-iron with the interval you found for the wedge. Do you wish to modify your advice to Josh? Explain.

Core Connections, Course 2

8-21. Mr. Webb has only one more starting position available on his basketball team, but two students have tried out for it. He wants to choose the student who is likely to score the most points.
The two students from whom he can choose are described below.

a. In her most recent games, Jana scored: 7 46 9 6 11 7 9 11 19 7 9 11 9 55 11 7 points, while Alejandra scored 13 15 9 18 13 17 17 15 points. Which girl has the higher average (mean) number of points?

b. Which student do you think Mr. Webb should select and why? Use parallel box plots (two box plots on the same number line) to support your explanation.

c. Why was the mean not a good measure of the girl's typical performance?

d. Calculate the IQR to measure the variability of each girl's performance.

e. Who had the higher median and by how many points? How large is the difference between the medians measured by how many IQRs would fit into it?

8-22. Gregory and his sister shared a computer at home. In order to be fair, they kept track of how much time they spent socializing with friends each day for the last two weeks. Their usage in minutes follows:

Gregory: 49 48 51 52 68 40 73 68 61 60 69 55 51 59

His sister: 49 45 37 63 56 57 62 50 42 48 55 64 40 42

Make a parallel box plot to compare their usage. Is their median usage notably different from each other? If the usage is notably different, how much more did one of them use the computer than the other, measured in number of IQRs?

Ⓜ️ ETHODS AND MEANINGS

MATH NOTES

Comparing Box Plots

One way to visually represent a distribution of collected data is with a **combination histogram and box plot**. The box plot is graphed on the same *x*-axis as the histogram. See Alejandro's scores at right.

To compare two distributions, a second combination histogram and box plot is drawn *with the same scale* as the first histogram. The two combination plots can then be lined up exactly on top of each other so that differences are readily observable. Compare Alejandro's scores from above to César's scores at right.

Sometimes comparing only the two box plots is enough to be able to compare the distributions. When two box plots are drawn on the same axis, they are called **parallel box plots**. An example is shown at right.

Alejandro's Scores

César's Scores

8-23. The two histograms below show how precisely Lue threw 50 darts with his right hand and then 50 with his left hand. Study the two histograms.

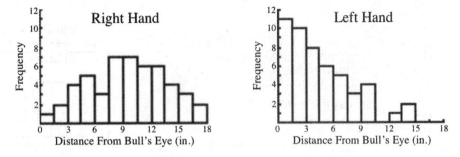

a. Estimate what the box plots would look like and make a parallel box plot.

b. Compare the center, shape, spread, and outliers between Lue's left hand and right hand.

c. Is Lue more precise throwing with his right hand or with his left hand?

d. Use the box plot to estimate how many IQRs above the median Lue's better hand is. Explain your thinking.

8-24. Find the missing lengths or values on the diagram below. Assume that the line is evenly divided.

8-25. Joaquin has agreed to lend his younger brother $45 so that he can buy a new tank for his pet lizard. Joaquin is charging his brother 2% simple interest per month. If his brother pays him back in 6 months, how much will Joaquin get back?

8-26.   Michaela holds her state high school record for the 500-meter freestyle swimming event. She can swim the event in 4 minutes and 50 seconds. At this same rate, how far will she swim in 10 minutes?

8-27.   Mrs. Chen has two brothers. Mark is 7 years older than Mrs. Chen and Eric is 11 years younger than Mrs. Chen. The sum of all three of their ages is 149. Use the 5-D Process to determine the age of Mrs. Chen.

8-28.   For each equation below, solve for x. Show the process you use to check your answer.

a. $2\frac{1}{2} = x - 1\frac{1}{4}$ b. $5x = 2x + 12$ c. $x - 14.6 = 8.02$

$8.2.1$ Is the survey fair?

Is it a good sample?

Representative Samples

If you want to know what a bowl of soup tastes like, do you need to eat all of the soup in the bowl? Or can you get a good idea of the taste by trying a small sample?

When you conduct a survey, it is not usually possible for you to survey every person in the **population** you are interested in, such as *all* female teenage shoppers or *all* of the students at your school. Instead, statisticians collect information about a **sample** (a portion) of the population. However, finding a **representative sample** (a sample that represents the whole population well) is not easy.

8-29.   As the social director of the Class Council, Ramin would like to survey a few students about their interests.

When Ramin analyzes the results from the survey, he wants to make claims about the interests of *all* of the students in his school. If he were to survey only students on the Class Council, for example, it might be hard to make claims about what all students think. Students who are on the Class Council may not have the same social interests as other students. Consider this idea as you think about the samples described below.

   a.   If Ramin wanted to generalize the opinions of all students at his school, would it make sense to go to the grocery store and survey the people there? Why or why not?

   b.   If he wanted to generalize the opinions of all students at his school, would it make sense to ask all of his friends at school? Why or why not?

   c.   If he wanted to generalize the opinions of all students at his school, would it make sense to ask every third person who entered the cafeteria at lunch? Why or why not?

8-30.   There are a variety of ways to choose samples of
         the population you are studying. Every sample
         has features that make it more or less
         representative of the larger population. For
         example, if you want to represent all of the
         students at your school, but you survey all of the
         students at school 30 minutes after the last class
         has ended, you are likely to get a disproportionate
         number of students who play school sports,
         attend after-school activities, or go to after-school tutoring.

   a.   If you ask the opinion of the people around you, then you have used a
        convenience sample. If you took a convenience sample right now, what
        would be some features of the sample? Would you expect a convenience
        sample to represent the entire student population at your school? Why or
        why not?

   b.   If you email or create an online questionnaire then you have used a
        voluntary response sample. What are some features of the people in a
        volunteer response sample? Could it represent the sample of all of the
        students at school accurately?

   c.   You use a **cluster sample** if you first divide the students into smaller
        groups so that each smaller group represents all of the students at your
        school. Then you randomly select one or more of these groups to
        sample. How might you divide the students at your school into groups that
        each represent the whole school? Explain. Are there any reasons that these
        clusters might not be fully representative of all the students at your school?

8-31.   From what population is each of these samples taken? Write down the actual
         population for each of these sampling techniques.

Method of Sampling	Description of Actual Population
Call every hundredth name in the phone book.	People with phones who also have their numbers listed
Survey people who come to the "Vote Now" booth at the high school football game.	
Ask every tenth student entering a high school football game.	
Haphazardly survey students during the morning break.	
Text response to an online "instant" poll.	
Hand out surveys in the library before school.	
Survey all students in Period 1 English classes.	

8-32.	A study at the University of Iowa in 2008 concluded that children that play violent video games are more aggressive in real life. Children ages 9 to 12 were studied to determine how much they played violent video games; peers and teachers were asked how much these students hit, kicked, and got into fights with other students.

a.	Can you legitimately conclude from this study that teenagers who play violent video games tend to be more aggressive? Why or why not?

b.	Can you legitimately conclude from this study that children ages 9 to 12 who play violent video games are more likely to commit violent crimes? Why or why not?

c.	Can you legitimately conclude from this study that children ages 9 to 12 who play violent video games tend to hit and kick more in school?

d.	Can you legitimately conclude from this study that playing a lot of violent video games will cause 9 to 12-year-old students to become more violent at school?

8-33.	Addie was helping children in a kindergarten class learn to read. She was curious how old the typical child was when they entered kindergarten. It was not practical to look up the school records of all 100 kindergarteners. So on the first day of school, Addie took a sample: she asked the parent of the first fifteen students to be dropped off at the school how old (in months) their child was. Her data is listed below.

67 61 69 72 71 65 67 67 57 68 71 72 61 59 62

Make an **inference** (a statistical prediction) of the mean age of Kindergarten children at the school.

8-34.	**Additional Challenge:** Create a survey question that will help you to better know the students in your school. Tell when and where you would ask the question so that you asked a representative sample of the students in the school.

METHODS AND MEANINGS

Types of Samples from a Population

When taking a survey, the **population** is the group of people about whom the information is to be gathered. For example, if you wanted to conduct a survey about what foods to serve in the cafeteria, the population would be the entire student body. Since it is not usually convenient to survey the total population, different kinds of **samples** may be used.

A **representative sample** is a subgroup of the population that matches the general characteristics of the entire population. If you choose to sample 10% of the students, you would need to include an equivalent fraction of students from each grade and an equivalent ratio of male to female students as the larger population.

A **convenience sample** is a subgroup of the population where it is easy to collect data. Only sampling the students in your homeroom, for example, would be convenient, but would not necessarily accurately represent the entire school.

A **cluster sample** is a subgroup of the population that contains a common characteristic. Sampling only the eighth graders, in the above example, would be a cluster sample. Again, this sample would not necessarily represent the entire school.

A **voluntary response sample** contains only the sample of the population that chose to respond. This also would not necessarily represent the entire population.

8-35.   Suppose you were conducting a survey to try to determine what portion of voters in your small town support a particular candidate for mayor. Consider each of the following methods for sampling the voting population of your town. State whether each is likely to produce a representative sample and explain your reasoning.

   a.   Ask every voter on your block.

   b.   Randomly pick one house from each block in the neighborhood and survey the homeowner.

   c.   Survey each person at the I-Jump Pancake Restaurant after church on Sunday morning.

   d.   Ask people who are leaving the twice-yearly town hall meeting.

   e.   Visit every tenth person on the county's voter registration list.

8-36.   Calculate the percent change in each problem below.

   a.   Robert wanted to buy a computer game that cost $25 last week. This week when he went back to buy the game, the price was $35. What was the percent of increase in the price?

   b.   Susan bought a jacket on sale. The original price of $35 was marked down to $25. What was the percent discount because of the sale?

   c.   Why were your answers to parts (a) and (b) different?

8-37.   Simplify each expression.

   a. $\frac{12}{5} \div \frac{7}{10}$ b. $\frac{9}{4} \div (-\frac{1}{3})$ c. $-\frac{3}{5} \div (-\frac{1}{6})$

8-38.   Find the area and perimeter of each shape below. Show your steps and work.
          Note: Diagrams are not drawn to scale.

a.   b.

8-39.   The recommended speed on a scenic road is 35 mph. Driving too fast is a
          hazard, but so is driving too slowly. Safe speeds s may be described by the
          inequality $|35 - s| \le 10$.

          a.   Find a list of at least 5 safe speeds.

          b.   Determine how to show the entire set of possible values (solutions) for s by
               graphing them on a number line.

8-40.   Simplify and solve each equation below for x. Show your work and check your
          answer.

          a. $24 = 3x + 3$ b. $2(x - 6) = x - 14$

          c. $3(2x - 3) = 4x - 5$ d. $\frac{3}{4}x = 2x - 5$

8.2.2 How close is my sample?

Is it a good sample?

Inference from Random Samples

In the previous lesson, you studied the randomness of various sampling populations. If you wanted to know the average height of the trees in a forest, you would not want to measure every tree in the forest. You would take a sample of the trees and measure them to give you a good prediction of the average height of all the trees.

If you measured 10 trees and found the mean, you would get a number that describes those 10 trees, but how well does that number describe all of the trees in the entire forest? Let's investigate similar situations.

8-41. The sighting of American robins in yards is considered a sign that spring has arrived. You would like to know the average weight of an American robin in your town.

   a. Of course you cannot weigh every robin in town, even if you could figure out how to catch them all. A sample seems like a good idea. Read the Math Notes box, "Random Samples," that follows this lesson.

   Think about how you can take a random sample from the population of robins in the envelope provided by your teacher. What things would be important to do? Discuss this with your team.

   b. Now take a random sample of ten robins from your envelope and record their weights. Each member of your team should do the same thing with their own random sample.

   c. Calculate the mean of your sample. Do you think that your mean is representative of the population? What inferences can you make about the population from your sample?

   d. Compare your estimate of the population mean to the means of the other students in your team. Is your mean the true average weight for all American robins in town? Are any of your teammates' numbers the true average? How can you explain any differences between the means?

8-42.   Your estimate of the mean will probably be a little larger or smaller than the true average weight of robins. Let's explore how much larger or smaller your estimate might be than the true average.

a.   Follow your teacher's directions to add your estimate of the population mean to the list with the rest of the class' estimates. Then, make a combination histogram and box plot of the data. Use a bin width of 5g on your histogram.

b.   What causes variation in the sample means? That is, why are some of the sample means on your class graph so much larger or smaller than others? Why are so many of the sample means bunched up in the middle?

c.   Within what interval do you suppose is the true mean weight of American robins?

8-43.   Cyrus plays volleyball in county-wide tournaments. He wondered what portion of volleyball players prefer plain water over sports drinks during intense games.

a.   At his next tournament, Cyrus selected 50 random players from all the teams to ask about their preference. 78% preferred plain water. What inference can Cyrus make about *all* the volleyball players in the county?

b.   What additional information would Cyrus gain if it was practical to take many samples at many tournaments in the county?

c.   If many samples could be taken, the distribution of percentages in each of the samples might look like this:

% preferring water: 84% 71% 73% 83% 80% 80%

79% 77% 81% 72% 81% 78%

Make a box plot of the sample means. With this additional information, make a new statement about volleyball players and water.

8-44.   LEARNING LOG

Make an entry in your Learning Log titled "Inferences From Random Samples" and add today's date. Then discuss with your team and answer the following questions for your Learning Log entry. Why would you want to take a sample instead of just testing the entire population? What is the best way to take a sample from a population? Why are random samples more representative of the population than other kinds of samples? What additional information would you have if you could take many samples from the same population? What information can you get from a random sample?

Review & Preview

8-45. Athena was working on her Girl Scout silver award and was wondering what percentage of people support the Girl Scouts financially through cookie sales outside the grocery store.

At the next cookie sale, Athena kept track of how many customers at the grocery store walked by the cookie table and how many stopped to purchase cookies. 32% of families stopped and purchased cookies at the table.

Athena continued collecting data at several different grocery stores around town. Here are the percent of those who bought cookies at each store:

32% 29% 19% 31% 30% 24% 38% 33% 42% 25% 22% 27%

Make a box plot of the samples, then make a new statement about what proportion of people (in what interval) you can expect to buy Girl Scout cookies at the grocery store.

8-46.   Bee is tiling her kitchen floor using square tiles that are 1 foot long on each side. The rectangular floor is 13 feet by 7 feet.

   a.   If she has 86 tiles, does she have enough to cover the floor? If not, how many more does she need?

   b.   Does she have enough to tile just around the edges of the kitchen? If so, how many leftover tiles will she have? If not, how many more will she need? Draw a picture and show your work.

8-47.   Draw an isosceles trapezoid (a trapezoid with two equal, non-parallel sides). Label the top base 6 cm and the height 4 cm. If the area of this trapezoid is 36 square cm, what is the length of the other base? You may find it helpful to use the 5-D Process to write an equation to solve.

8-48.   Simplify each expression.

   a. $\frac{5}{12} + (-\frac{7}{8}) - (-\frac{1}{6})$ b. $-\frac{11}{15} - \frac{4}{5} - (-\frac{57}{60})$ c. $4\frac{1}{12} + (-1\frac{5}{6})$

   d. $-\frac{7}{11} \cdot \frac{8}{9}$ e. $\frac{1}{3} \cdot \frac{1}{2} + \frac{5}{6}$ f. $-\frac{4}{6} \cdot (-\frac{9}{2})$

8-49.   Solve these equations for x. Check your answers.

   a. $2(x + 4.5) = 32$ b. $6 + 2.5x = 21$ c. $\frac{x}{9} = \frac{5}{16}$

8-50.   Autumn and her friends had dinner at their favorite restaurant, and the bill came to $60. They decided to leave 18% of the bill for a tip. Without using a calculator, help them compute how much money is 18% of the bill.

8.3.1 What is an angle?

Introduction to Angles

Have you ever watched a dance team performing a routine in which each person moves and spins in perfect unison? Each dancer always knows exactly how many times to turn and the direction in which he or she should end up facing. In this lesson, you will develop ways to describe turns by investigating angles and look at angles inside shapes.

8-51.   MY HEAD IS SPINNING!

What does it mean to "do a three-sixty (360)"?
What about "a one-eighty (180)"?

a.   Your teacher will instruct you to stand up and "do a 360," that is, to turn 360°. Then your teacher will instruct you to "do a 180," that is, to turn 180°.

b.   Work with your team to design a clear and consistent way to draw diagrams to represent these movements. Be sure your diagrams include something that shows the direction a person would face at the beginning and the end of the turn as well as the size of the turn in between.

c.   What would it mean to "do a 90," or to turn 90°? What about "a 45"? Add diagrams for these movements. Be prepared to explain your diagrams to the class.

8-52.   When your teacher asked you to "do a 360," how did you know what to do? "360" refers to turning in a full circle, that is, turning completely around right back to where you started. The most common unit used to measure rotation is a **degree** and there are 360 degrees in one full rotation.

Get a copy of the Lesson 8.3.1A Resource Page, which has a diagram of the angle shown at right. Work with your team to *estimate* the measure of this angle in degrees. Be prepared to explain how you determined your estimate.

8-53.   ANGLE RULERS

How can you measure angles accurately using degrees? In this activity, you will build a device (you can call it an "angle ruler") to help you measure angles in degrees.

Your Task: Get a copy of the Lesson 8.3.1B Resource Page, which contains a diagram like the one at right. Work with your team to find a way to fold and label the resource page multiple times to make it into an "angle ruler." The ruler is started with 0° and includes a mark for 180°. Be sure to design your angle ruler so that you can measure common angles such as 30°, 45°, 60°, 90° and 135°. Be prepared to explain your strategy.

Discussion Points

How can we partition it into pieces of equal angle?

How big is this angle in degrees?

Can we subdivide it any further?

8-54.   Use your new "angle ruler" to measure the angle you estimated in problem 8-52. Check with your teacher to see if your measurement is reasonable. How accurate is your new measurement tool?

8-55.   Actually, "angle rulers" exist. They are called **protractors**.

a. Get a protractor from your teacher. Compare it with the one that you made. In what ways are they similar and in what ways are they different?

b. Hunter used a protractor to measure the angle at right. He got 60°. Is his answer reasonable? Explain why or why not.

c. When measuring an angle with a protractor, is it necessary to line up one side of the angle with the 0° or 180° mark? If you did not, how would you figure out what the measure of the angle was? Explain.

Core Connections, Course 2

8-56.   Estimate the angles formed in the diagrams below *without measuring*. Be ready to explain your estimates.

a.   b.

c.   d.

8-57.   Angles can be thought of as the result of a rotation or turn. They can also help you to describe shapes.

Get a Lesson 8.3.1C Resource Page, which has larger diagrams of each of the figures below. First *estimate*, then *measure* the indicated angles in degrees.

a.   b.   c.

8-58.   UNIQUE UNITS

Additional Challenge: Does a complete rotation *have to be* broken into exactly 360 small parts? What if you used a different unit?

a.   Work with your team to invent a *new* unit to measure angles. Give it a name and decide how many of your units fit into a full circle.

b.   Draw diagrams to represent angles resulting from a full turn, a half-turn, a quarter-turn, and $\frac{1}{8}$ of a turn and then label the measurement of each angle with your new unit. Be prepared to share your diagrams with the rest of the class and to explain how to measure with your unit.

c.   Examine the diagram at right. Estimate the measure of this angle in your new unit. Be prepared to explain how you got your estimate.

8-59.   LEARNING LOG

In your Learning Log, explain what an angle is and how you can estimate the measure of an angle in degrees. Include diagrams to explain your thinking. Title this entry "Angles" and label it with today's date.

MᴇᴛHODS AND Mᴇᴀɴɪɴɢꜱ

MATH NOTES

Angles

To understand the meaning of an angle, picture two rays starting at a single point called the **vertex** of the angle, as shown in the diagram at right. (A **ray** is a part of a line that starts at a point and goes on without end in one direction.) An **angle** is formed by two rays (or line segments) that have the same starting point (or **endpoint**). The **measure** of an angle is how many degrees you rotate your starting ray to get to the ray on the opposite side of an angle. One way to visualize an angle is as a measure of how "open" the gap is between the two rays.

Angles are named by their size in comparison to a right angle. That is, they are named according to whether they are less than, greater than, or equal to a right angle. An **acute angle** measures less than 90°. An **obtuse angle** measures more than 90° and less than 180°. The little box in an angle indicates that it is a **right angle**, which measures 90°). A **straight angle** measures 180° and forms a straight line.

acute angle   right angle   obtuse angle   straight angle

Review & Preview

8-60.   Estimate the measure of each angle below.

a.   b.   c.   d.

460

Core Connections, Course 2

8-61. Write an equation that represents each diagram below and find the value of the variable.

a.

b.

8-62. Simplify each expression.

a. $\frac{9}{15} \div \frac{4}{3}$

b. $-\frac{19}{20} + \frac{4}{5}$

c. $-\frac{8}{9} \div (-\frac{2}{5})$

d. $3\frac{1}{2} \div 1\frac{1}{7}$

e. $-\frac{3}{4} - (-\frac{11}{16})$

f. $\frac{2}{9} \cdot \frac{14}{15} \cdot (-\frac{9}{10})$

g. $-10\frac{4}{5} + (-\frac{3}{8})$

h. $\frac{12}{5} \div (-\frac{1}{10})$

8-63. Ms. Carpenter asked each of her students to record how much time it takes them to get from school to home this afternoon. The next day, students came back with this data, in minutes: 15, 12, 5, 55, 6, 9, 47, 8, 35, 3, 22, 26, 46, 54, 17, 42, 43, 42, 15, 5.

a. Create a combination histogram and box plot to display this information. Use a bin width of 10 minutes.

b. Find the mean and the median. Why does neither plot seem very adequate in describing the center of this distribution? How could you better describe a "typical" trip home?

c. Considering the situation, make a conjecture as to why this data has a shape with two peaks.

8-64. Kirk's grandparents are really enjoying their portable music players and have downloaded many more albums. Maude now has 225 albums, 135 of which are heavy metal. Claude now has 450 albums, 270 of which are heavy metal. Which of Kirk's grandparents has a higher probability of listening to heavy metal?

8-65. Josue called his father to say that he was almost home. He had traveled 61.5 miles, which was $\frac{3}{4}$ of the way home. Write and solve an equation to calculate the total distance he will travel to get home.

8.3.2 What kind of angle is it?

If you look around you, you will see angles everywhere. Angles are important in construction, sports, and art. In the previous lesson, you learned how to measure angles using a protractor. Today you will classify angles and use your protractor to identify special angles.

8-66. In geometry, an **angle** is formed by two rays with a common endpoint. A **ray** is a line that has an endpoint and extends infinitely in a particular direction. The point where the two rays intersect is called the **vertex** of the angle.

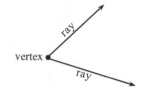

One of the most common angles is a right angle. A **right angle** measures 90°. If an angle measures less than 90°, it is called an **acute angle**. If an angle measures more than 90° but less than 180°, it is called an **obtuse angle**.

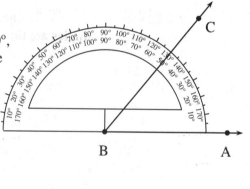

Use a protractor to find the measure of each angle, and then classify it according to its measure.

a.   b.   c.

d. A straight line is also called a **straight angle**. Draw a straight angle on your paper. What is the measure of a straight angle?

8-67. The diagrams below show some students' use of protractors. Explain what each student needs to do to find the correct angle measure.

a.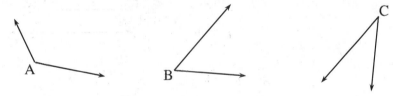

b.

c.

m∠ = 60°

d.

8-68. **Complementary angles** are two angles with a sum of 90°.

Supplementary angles are two angles with a sum of 180°.

a. Use your protractor to measure each of the angles below and determine which angles are complementary and which angles are supplementary.

A   B   C

b. With your team, come up with a strategy for remembering the definitions of complementary and supplementary.

8-69.   ADJACENT ANGLES

Angles that share that same vertex and one side are referred to as **adjacent angles**. "Adjacent" in the English language means "next to." For two angles to be adjacent, they must satisfy the following three conditions:

1.   The two angles must have a common (shared or same) side.

2.   They must have a common vertex (a common starting point for all sides).

3.   They can have no interior points in common (no overlap is permitted). The common side must be between the two angles.

Copy each of the figures below onto your paper. Determine which pairs of angles are adjacent and which are not by checking to see if each angle pair satisfies all three conditions. Write "yes" or "no" next to each figure. If you write "no," give a short explanation.

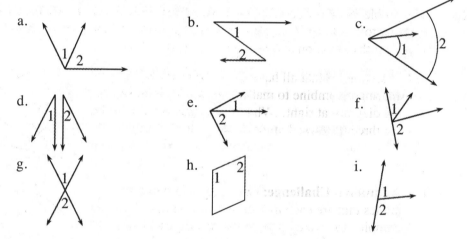

8-70.   VERTICAL ANGLES

Angles formed by two intersecting lines that are not adjacent are called **vertical angles**. In the diagram at right, angles 1 and 2 are vertical angles.

a.   What can you say about angles 3 and 4?

b.   Use your protractor to measure each of the four angles. What do you notice?

c.   Draw a pair of vertical angles on your paper. Each team member should draw angles with different measures. Measure your vertical angles. What do you think is true about the measures of vertical angles?

8-71. Find the measure of the missing angles.

a. $\angle 1 = 75°$

$\angle 2 = ?$

b. $\angle 1 = 55°$

$\angle 2 = ?$

c. $\angle 1$ and $\angle 2$ are complementary

$\angle 1 = 27°$

$\angle 2 = ?$

d. $\angle 1$ and $\angle 2$ are supplementary

$\angle 1 = 30°$

$\angle 2 = ?$

8-72. The problems below describe other situations where some angles have been put together to create larger angles. For each problem below, write an equation to represent the situation and then answer the question.

a. Three angles that all have the same measure and one 36° angle combine to make a 90° angle, as shown in the diagram at right. What is the measure of each of the three unmarked angles?

b. **Additional Challenge:** One angle and two other angles that are each half as large as the first combine to create an angle that measures 140°, as shown in the diagram at right. What are the measures of each of the angles?

8-73. **Additional Challenge:** Determine the size of all of the angles labeled with variables.

METHODS AND MEANINGS

Angle Relationships

It is common to identify angles using three letters. For example, $\angle ABC$ means the angle you would find by going from point A, to point B, to point C in the diagram at right. Point B is the **vertex** of the angle (where the endpoints of the two sides meet) and $\overrightarrow{BA}$ and $\overrightarrow{BC}$ are the rays that define it. A **ray** is a part of a line that has an endpoint (starting point) and extends infinitely in one direction.

If two angles have measures that add up to 90°, they are called **complementary angles**. For example, in the diagram above right, $\angle ABC$ and $\angle CBD$ are complementary because together they form a right angle.

If two angles have measures that add up to 180°, they are called **supplementary angles**. For example, in the diagram at right, $\angle EFG$ and $\angle GFH$ are supplementary because together they form a straight angle.

Two angles do not have to share a vertex to be complementary or supplementary. The first pair of angles at right are supplementary; the second pair of angles are complementary.

120°   60°   **Supplementary**   50°   40°   **Complementary**

Adjacent angles are angles that have a common vertex, share a common side, and have no interior points in common. So $\angle c$ and $\angle d$ in the diagram at right are adjacent angles, as are $\angle c$ and $\angle f$, $\angle f$ and $\angle g$, and $\angle g$ and $\angle d$.

Vertical angles are the two opposite (that is, non-adjacent) angles formed by two intersecting lines, such as angles $\angle c$ and $\angle g$ in the diagram above right. $\angle c$ by itself is not a vertical angle, nor is $\angle g$, although $\angle c$ and $\angle g$ together are a pair of vertical angles. Vertical angles always have equal measure.

8-74. Alexander and Santiago put five pattern blocks together with one vertex of each block touching, as shown in the diagram at right. Work with your team to find the measure of the smaller angle of a beige rhombus.

8-75. Use the vocabulary terms you learned today to classify the following angle pairs. Use the terms complementary, supplementary, adjacent, and vertical.

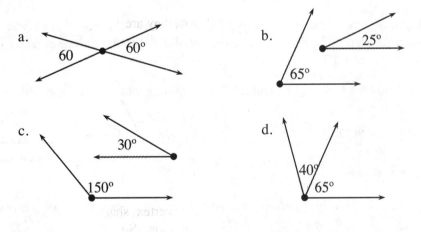

a.

b.

c.

d.

8-76. Graph the following points on a coordinate graph: $A(-3,-3)$, $B(3,0)$, $C(3,6)$, $D(-3,6)$. Connect the points as you plot them. Then connect point A to point D.

a. Describe the shape you have created.

b. Identify the types of angles at points A, B, C, and D.

8-77.   Scientists studying prehistoric birds have estimated the weights (in grams) of
         two different sub-species of birds. The data they collected is shown below.

         Pre-emergent thrushes:
                  49, 54, 52, 58, 61, 72, 73, 78, 73, 82, 83, 73, 61, 67, 68

         Post-emergent thrushes:
                  65, 35, 48, 29, 57, 87, 94, 68, 86, 73, 58, 74, 85, 91, 88, 97

         a.   Create a parallel box plot to compare the weights of these two sub-species
              of birds.

         b.   Would the mean accurately represent the middle of the data? Why or why
              not?

         c.   A fossil of a bird is found. Scientists estimated that its weight must have
              been around 75 grams. Which sub-species was the bird most likely a
              member of? Explain.

8-78.   A candy store's specialty is taffy. Customers can fill a bag with taffy and the
         price is based on how much the candy weighs. The store charges $2 for
         10 ounces of taffy.

         a.   Copy the table below and fill in the missing values. Add three more
              entries.

Amount of taffy (ounces)	2	5	10	12	15	20
Price ($)			$2			$4

         b.   Graph the values in the table. Let x represent the number of ounces and
              y represent the price in dollars.

         c.   Is this situation proportional? Explain your reasoning.

8-79.   Write an equation to represent this situation and answer the question. Use the
         5-D Process to help you define a variable and write an equation if necessary.

         Ella is trying to determine the side lengths of a triangle. She knows that the
         longest side is three times longer than the shortest side. The medium side is ten
         more than twice the shortest side. If the perimeter is 142 cm, how long is each
         side?

Core Connections, Course 2

8.3.3 How can I build it?

Constructing Shapes

Architects and drafters make careful drawings of the buildings that
they design. The drawings represent how the building should be
constructed. They show the thickness of the walls and where
doors, windows, and pipes will be. To make these precise
diagrams, professionals often use special computer software.
However, some architects still prefer to draw diagrams by hand at
least some of the time. They use special drawing tools that look
something like those in the drawing at right, including a right
triangle tool and a protractor.

Building plans are just one example of a precise geometric drawing. Mathematicians have
used these basic tools to draw accurate diagrams for other reasons. In mathematics,
making a **construction** is the process of using a straightedge and compass to solve a
problem or create a geometric diagram. Constructing shapes that meet different
guidelines can help you understand many of the specific characteristics of those shapes.
In this lesson, you will use given conditions to construct your own shapes.

8-80. Without looking at anyone else's work, each member of your team should draw
a triangle with one angle that measures 60° and one side that is 1.5 cm long.

    a. When each member of your team has finished, check the drawings of your
teammates by trading papers and measuring the sides and angles. Does
everyone have a triangle that matches the given description? If not, come
up with a strategy for drawing accurately sized angles and line segments.
Are all of the triangles the same as one another?

    b. Measure each of the three angles in your triangle. What is the sum of the
three angles? Share your answer with your team. Make a conjecture about
the sum of the angles in a triangle.

8-81.   Again, without looking at each others papers, have each member of your team draw a quadrilateral with one angle that measures 30°, one angle that measures 60°, and one side that is 5 cm long.

      a.   Again, when each member of your team is finished, check the drawings of your teammates by trading papers and measuring the sides and angles. Does everyone have a quadrilateral that matches the given description? Are all of the quadrilaterals the same as one another?

      b.   Measure each of the four angles in your quadrilateral. What is the sum of the four angles? Share your answer with your team. Make a conjecture about the sum of the angles in a quadrilateral.

8-82.   All measurements have a small degree of error and measurements made by people can vary quite a bit as you discovered in Lesson 8.1.1 and 8.1.2. Using technology to construct shapes can give you more accurate information and allow you to test more situations more quickly.

      a.   First, check your conclusions from problem 8-80 using technology. Work with a partner to make a triangle with the same conditions as those given in problem 8-80 using the technology tool (or the Lesson 8.3.3 Resource Page). Verify your results from problem 8-80. That is, does each of your triangles look the same as the one that you made in problem 8-80? Is the sum of the angles for each triangle still the same?

      b.   Now use the same technology tool or resource page materials to create the quadrilaterals that you and your partner made in problem 8-81. Again, verify your results that the quadrilaterals look the same as those that you made by hand and that the sum of angles for each is the same.

8-83.   On your own, write down two specific conditions for a triangle. Then trade papers with someone in your team and draw the triangle specified. Check to see if your partner drew the triangle correctly. If they did not, verbally help them to draw it correctly. Do not draw the triangle for them.

8-84.   On your own, write down three specific conditions for a drawing a quadrilateral. Then trade paper with a different person in your team and have them draw your quadrilateral. Check to see if they drew the quadrilateral correctly. If they did not, verbally help them to draw it correctly. Do not draw the quadrilateral for them.

Core Connections, Course 2

METHODS AND MEANINGS

Circle Vocabulary

The **radius** of a circle is a line segment from its center to any point on the circle. The term is also used for the length of these segments. More than one radius are called **radii**.

A **chord** of a circle is a line segment joining any two points on a circle.

A **diameter** of a circle is a chord that goes through its center. The term is also used for the length of these chords. The length of a diameter is twice the length of a radius.

Review & Preview

8-85.   Draw angles that approximate each of the following measures.

a.   50°   b.   170°   c.   190°   d.   270°

8-86.   Use a straightedge to draw a triangle on your paper.

a.   Estimate the measure of each angle in your triangle and label it.

b.   Add your three estimated angle measures. What do you notice? Do you need to change any of your estimates?

8-87.   Read the Math Notes box for this lesson and then find the length of the radius and diameter of each of the following circles.

a.   3 cm   b.   3 in.   c.   1 mm

8-88.   Tino works at a retail clothing store as a sales clerk and part of his paycheck is based on commission, meaning that it is determined by the value of the clothes that he sells. Each week, he earns $7 an hour plus 15% of his total sales. If Tino works for 18 hours and sells $538 in clothes in a certain week, what is the amount of his commission? What is his total pay for that week?

8-89.   Write and solve a proportion for the following problem.

In a recent survey for the student council, Dominique found that 150 students out of a total of 800 students on campus did *not* like soda. If half of the student body was going to attend a dance, how many students could she expect would want soda?

8-90.   Find the value of each variable in the following figures. Do not use a protractor. Use the properties of angles to help you.

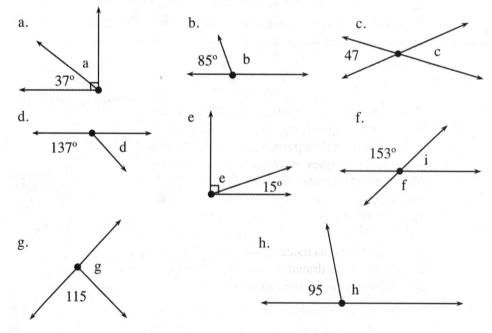

8.3.4 How many triangles can I make?

Building Triangles

Triangles are important shapes. They are the basic building blocks of many architectural designs and structural supports. A tripod stool will tend to be more stable than a chair with four legs. This is because of triangles!

In Lesson 8.3.3 you became familiar with the technology tool for building shapes and gained some basic information about angles in triangles and quadrilaterals. Today, you will do a more in-depth investigation of triangles, you will learn about when a triangle can and cannot be made, and you will discover the necessary condition to create a unique triangle.

8-91. How many different "parts" does a triangle have that can be specified or measured? What are these parts?

8-92. How many different triangles do you think that you can make specifying only two measures to use for the triangle's parts, such as one angle and one side, two angles, or two sides? Work with a partner to investigate this question using the technology tool (or the Lesson 8.3.3 Resource Page materials). Each person will attempt to build a triangle with the specified angle measures and/or side lengths listed below without looking at their partner's drawing. For each triangle that you build and each set of conditions given, do the following:

- Compare the triangle that you built to one that your partner built and decide whether they are the same or not. Are your triangles the same or different? Are there any other possible triangles that can be built using the same conditions? State your conclusion.

- Sketch the triangle(s) on your paper, labeling the given angles or side lengths.

a. One side length 4.5 cm and one angle 135°

b. Two angles: 90° and 60°

c. Two side lengths: 4.5 cm and 7 cm

8-93.   Discuss with your team whether or not knowing only two of the six possible measurements for the parts of any triangle is enough information to always draw *exactly* the same triangle. Test your conjecture with more examples until your team is satisfied that you are accurate. Write a summary of your conclusions and your reasons for them.

8-94.   Imagine now that three possible measures for a triangle's six parts (3 angles or 3 side lengths) are given. Do you think that everyone will make the same triangle in that case?

   a.   First, investigate this question for three possible side lengths given. Follow the same instructions as you did in problem 8-92 including building, sketching and labeling the figure(s) you make as well as stating your conclusion for each part. Use the technology tool or the Lesson 8.3.3 Resource Page.

         i.   1.5 cm, 5 cm, and 4.5 cm.

         ii.   4.5 cm, 5 cm, and 7 cm.

         iii. 1.5 cm, 4.5 cm, and 7 cm.

   b.   At this point, what do you think must be true about the sides of a triangle in order to create at least one triangle? Write down your ideas. Then work with your team to test your ideas by selecting at least 3 more sets of side lengths and trying to build triangles with them.

   c.   Discuss with your team whether knowing any three possible side lengths for a triangle is enough information for everyone to draw *exactly* the same triangle. Write a summary of your conclusions and your reasons for them.

Core Connections, Course 2

8-95.   Now investigate this same question for angles. That is, do you think that everyone will make the same triangle when given 3 angle measurements?

   a.   One more time, follow the same instructions as you did in problem 8-92 including building, sketching and labeling the figure(s) you make as well as stating your conclusion for each part. Use the technology tool or the Lesson 8.3.3 Resource Page.

      i.   90°, 60°, and 30°.

      ii.   90°, 45° and 45°.

      iii.   135°, 45°, and 60°.

   b.   At this point, what do you think must be true about the angle measurements in order to create at least one triangle? Write down your ideas. Then work with your team to test your ideas by selecting at least 3 more sets of angle measurements and trying to build triangles with them.

   c.   Discuss with your team whether or not knowing all 3 of the angles of a triangle is enough information for everyone to draw *exactly* the same triangle. Write a summary of your conclusions and your reasons for them.

8-96.   In problem 8-94 you found that if you are given three lengths to build the sides of a triangle, then if a triangle can be formed, all the triangles you could make were the same. Suppose you start with two triangles knowing that their three pairs of corresponding sides are the same, as shown in the diagram below.

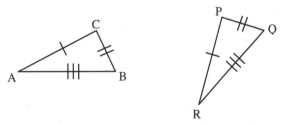

   a.   Examine the diagram. What do you think the markings indicate? Name the pairs of corresponding sides.

   b.   What can you say about the two triangles and why? What can you say about their angles? Why?

8-97.   LEARNING LOG

In this lesson, you learned a lot of important information
about triangles. You learned about the necessary
conditions for side lengths and angles to make a triangle.
You also learned how to determine if a triangle you create under given
conditions would automatically be the same as everyone else's triangle. You
will study these concepts in more detail in later math courses.

Make an entry in your Learning Log that summarizes your understanding at this
point. Include the following: How much information do you need to make a
triangle? Will that given information always create only one triangle, or could
it create many triangles? How can you tell how many different triangles can be
made, without actually trying to make the triangles? Title your entry
"Constructing Triangles" and include today's date.

METHODS AND MEANINGS

MATH NOTES

Triangle Inequality

For any three lengths to form a triangle, the sum of the lengths
of any two sides must be greater than the length of the third side.

For example, the lengths 3 cm, 10 cm, and
11 cm will form a triangle because

$$3 + 10 > 11$$
$$3 + 11 > 10$$
$$10 + 11 > 3$$

The lengths 5 m, 7 m, and 15 m will
not form a triangle because $5 + 7 = 12$,
and $12 \not> 15$.

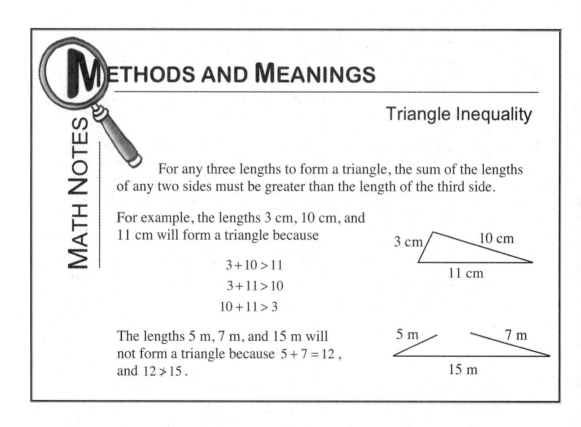

Core Connections, Course 2

8-98.   You learned in an earlier lesson how to classify an angle by comparing it to a
         90° right angle. Find the measure of each angle below and classify it according
         to its measure.

    a.   What is the measure of half of a right angle?

    b.   If the angle at right is made with a right angle
         added to half of a right angle, what is its measure?

    c.   Suppose a right angle is divided into three equal
         angles as shown at right. What is the measure of
         each angle?

8-99.   Gail bought a new baseball cap for $7.50, which was $\frac{1}{3}$ off the original price.
         What was the original price?

8-100.   Karla's traditional hybrid car gets 35% fewer miles per gallon than Jeenie's
         solar hybrid car. If Jeenie's car gets 60 miles per gallon, how many miles per
         gallon does Karla's car get? Calculate Karla's car's mileage in two different
         ways, using two different scale factors (multipliers).

8-101.   Adriel and Gustavo were playing a game with
         algebra tiles. As they compared them, they were
         left with the following expressions on their mats.
         Use legal moves to simplify what is on the mats.
         Be sure to record your work in a way that others
         can understand.

         Can you determine which side has the greater value? If so, show why. If not,
         for what values of x is Mat A larger?

8-102.   Find the numbers that belong in the Giant One in each problem to create an
         equivalent fraction. Copy each problem, and show the values you used within
         the Giant One.

    a. $\frac{7}{12} \cdot \boxed{} = \frac{56}{m}$ b. $\frac{8}{3} \cdot \boxed{} = \frac{n}{48}$ c. $\frac{20}{26} \cdot \boxed{} = \frac{k}{39}$ d. $\frac{20}{42} \cdot \boxed{} = \frac{50}{h}$

8-103.   A rental car company allows a customer to select any car available on the lot. Currently there are three blue sedans, two tan trucks, two black trucks, four red convertibles, four blue minivans, two black SUVs, and three tan hybrids. What is the probability a customer will select a black vehicle?

8-104.   Marley needs to construct a quadrilateral with side lengths of 2, 3, 4, and 5 centimeters. She thinks that there is only one possible quadrilateral that she can make. Is she correct?

8-105.   Use a ruler and a protractor to create a triangle with two sides of 3 cm each and an angle measuring 60°.

8-106.   Sketch each angle below on your paper, and label each one with its measure in degrees.

   a.   Identify whether each angle is an acute, obtuse, or right angle.

   b.   Which angles could form a complementary pair?

   c.   Which angles could form a supplementary pair?

8-107.   Evaluate each expression.

   a. $\frac{2(5+3)}{4}$

   b. $\frac{1}{2}(15+3)-10\div 2$

   c. $5\frac{1}{2}-2\frac{1}{4}+\frac{3}{8}$

   d. $3+\frac{3}{5}\cdot\frac{1}{4}$

   e. $-2+(-5+6)^2$

   f. $\frac{3}{4}\cdot\frac{1}{4}+\frac{5}{8}\cdot(-\frac{3}{2})$

8-108.   Draw a coordinate graph and plot the following points: $A(-1,-1)$, $B(2,2)$, $C(4,-2)$. Connect the points in order, and then connect point C to point A. Which point could you move to make this an obtuse triangle? (Remember that an obtuse triangle is a triangle with one angle greater than $90°$.) What would be the new point?

8-109.   This problem is a checkpoint for solving multi-step equations. It will be
          referred to as Checkpoint 8.

          Solve each equation.

    a. $24 = 3x + 3$ b. $6x + 12 = -x - 2$

    c. $3x + 3 - x + 2 = x + 5$ d. $5(x - 1) = 5(4x - 3)$

    Check your answers by referring to the Checkpoint 8 materials located at the
    back of your book.

    Ideally, at this point you are comfortable working with these types of problems
    and can solve them correctly. If you feel that you need more confidence when
    solving these types of problems, then review the Checkpoint 8 materials and try
    the practice problems provided. From this point on, you will be expected to do
    problems like these correctly and with confidence.

Chapter 8 Closure   What have I learned?

Reflection and Synthesis

The activities below offer you a chance to reflect about what
you have learned during this chapter. As you work, look for
concepts that you feel very comfortable with, ideas that you
would like to learn more about, and topics you need more
help with.

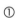   SUMMARIZING MY UNDERSTANDING

This section gives you an opportunity to show your understanding of how
variables can be used, one of the main ideas of this chapter.

Team Poster

You have been learning how to use variables
and write variable expressions in different
situations. You have done this to represent (1) a
missing piece of information and (2) a general
pattern or rule. You also learned strategies for
finding the value of the variable in a specific
situation as well as how to use the value given
to you to evaluate an expression. This section
gives you an opportunity to demonstrate what
you know so far about these concepts. Today
you and your team will create a poster that
illustrates the skills and knowledge that you
have developed in this area.

```
┌─────────────────────────────┐
│  ┌───────────────────────┐  │
│  │   Title               │  │
│  │                       │  │
│  └───────────────────────┘  │
│ Situations                  │
│  ┌──────────┬──────────┐    │
│  │          │          │    │
│  │          │          │    │
│  ├──────────┼──────────┤    │
│  │          │          │    │
│  │          │          │    │
│  └──────────┴──────────┘    │
│  Problem Statement and Solution │
│  ┌───────────────────────┐  │
│  │                       │  │
│  └───────────────────────┘  │
└─────────────────────────────┘
```

Brainstorm Situations: Follow your teacher's instructions to brainstorm a list
of different situations where a variable could be used to answer a question.

Situation Descriptions: Work with your team to think of four different
situations for which a variable could be used. Then each person should
write a description of one of the situations and suggest a variable to use for
the situation. Be sure to provide enough information so that someone
unfamiliar with the situation would understand what you mean.

Write a Problem: Follow your teacher's instructions to select one situation
randomly. Then work with your team to use that situation to write a
problem. Remember that you will need to provide all of the necessary
information and details for someone else to be able to solve the problem.
Show your problem to your teacher before the next step.

Activity continues on next page. →

①   *Activity continued from previous page.*

    Solve Your Problem: Now your team should find the answer to your problem. This should include writing a variable expression and then showing how to get the answer. Be sure to include your reasoning for your process and enough of your steps that anyone looking at them will know what you did.

    Team Poster: Follow the model above to label and construct the sections of your poster from the pieces that your team has created. Decide together on a title for your poster.

②   **WHAT HAVE I LEARNED?**

Doing the problems in this section will help you to evaluate which types of problems you feel comfortable with and which ones you need more help with.

Solve each problem as completely as you can. The table at the end of this closure section provides answers to these problems. It also tells you where you can find additional help and where to find practice problems like them.

CL 8-110.   Without a calculator, simplify each of the following expressions:

    a. $20 \div 2 + (-4)(-6)$ b. $5\frac{1}{2} \cdot 1\frac{1}{3}$

    c. $(0.4)(0.05)$ d. $\frac{4}{3} \div \frac{5}{8}$

    e. $2 + 4(-5) + \frac{1}{2}(3+9)$ f. $2(3+4(10-2))$

CL 8-111.   Find the missing angles in the diagrams below.

    a.   b.

         $27°$ $2x°$ $x°$ $142°$ $t°$

                                                 $a°$

                                         $c°$

CL 8-112.   Write an equation that represents each diagram and find the value of x.

a.

b.

CL 8-113.   Solve the proportion $\frac{22}{7} = \frac{5}{x}$ in two different ways. Show your work.

CL 8-114.   If baseball were played on Mars, the balls would fly much farther than they do on Earth. One could then speculate that the number of home runs hit would be much greater on Mars. Mike expects that he would hit 50% more home runs if he were playing baseball on Mars. If he hit 76 home runs on Earth, how many home runs does he expect he would hit on Mars?

CL 8-115.   Annika is saving money for a trip. She is able to save $75 a week. Her friend from Iceland, Eva, is also saving money. Eva is able to save 9000 Kronas (Icelandic money) each week. If $4 is equal to 509 Kronas, who is saving at a greater rate?

CL 8-116.   Use the 5-D Process to help you solve the following problem.

Lillian and Isabella went shopping for school supplies. Lillian found her favorite notebook on sale so she bought three of the exact same notebook. Isabella also wanted a notebook. She bought one of the same notebooks that Lillian bought. Both girls started shopping with the same amount of money. If Lillian spent all of her money and Isabella had $5 left, then how much money did each girl have when she arrived at the store?

CL 8-117.   In 1988 the Steering Committee of the Physicians Health Study Research Group released the results of a five-year experiment on over 22,000 male physicians aged 40 to 84. The research on this sample suggested that the participants who took an aspirin every other day had a lower rate of heart attacks.

Problem continues on next page. →

CL 8-117.   *Problem continued from previous page.*

    a.   Can you reasonably conclude from this sample that aspirin reduces heart attacks for all men and women? If you cannot conclude this, why not?

    b.   Can you reasonably conclude from this sample that aspirin reduces heart attacks for all men? If you cannot conclude this, why not?

    c.   Can you reasonably conclude from this sample that aspirin reduces heart attacks for all men aged 40 to 84? If you cannot conclude this, why not?

    d.   Can you reasonably conclude from this sample that aspirin reduces heart attacks for male physicians aged 40 to 84? If you cannot conclude this, why not?

    e.   Can you reasonably conclude from this sample that aspirin is good for male physicians aged 40 to 84? If you cannot conclude this, why not?

CL 8-118.   For each of the problems above, do the following:

- Draw a bar or number line that represents 0 to 10.

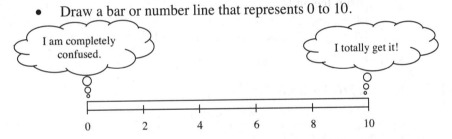

- Color or shade in a portion of the bar that represents your level of understanding and comfort with completing that problem on your own.

If any of your bars are less than a 5, choose *one* of those problems and do one of the following tasks:

- Write two questions that you would like to ask about that problem.

- Brainstorm two things that you DO know about that type of problem.

If all of your bars are at 5 or above, choose one problem and do one of these tasks:

- Write two questions you might ask or hints you might give to a student who was stuck on the problem.

- Make a new problem that is similar and more challenging than that problem and solve it.

WHAT TOOLS CAN I USE?

You have several tools and references available to help support your learning: your teacher, your study team, your math book, and your Toolkit, to name only a few. At the end of each chapter, you will have an opportunity to review your Toolkit for completeness. You will also revise or update it to reflect your current understanding of big ideas.

The main elements of your Toolkit should be your Learning Logs, Math Notes, and the vocabulary used in this chapter. Math words that are new appear in bold in the text. Refer to the lists provided below and follow your teacher's instructions to revise your Toolkit, which will help make it useful for you as you complete this chapter and as you work in future chapters.

Learning Log Entries

- Lesson 8.2.2 – Inferences From Random Samples
- Lesson 8.3.1 – Angles
- Lesson 8.3.4 – Constructing Triangles

Math Notes

- Lesson 8.1.2 – Comparing Box Plots
- Lesson 8.2.1 – Type of Samples from a Population
- Lesson 8.2.2 – Random Samples
- Lesson 8.3.1 – Angles
- Lesson 8.3.2 – Angle Relationships
- Lesson 8.3.3 – Circle Vocabulary
- Lesson 8.3.4 – Triangle Inequality

Mathematical Vocabulary

The following is a list of vocabulary found in this chapter. Some of the words have been seen in the previous chapter. The words in bold are words that are new to this chapter. Make sure that you are familiar with the terms below and know what they mean. For the words you do not know, refer to the glossary or index. You might also add these words to your Toolkit so that you can reference them in the future.

acute angle	**adjacent angles**	box plot
cluster sample	**complementary angles**	**construction**
convenience sample	**degree**	histogram
inference	interquartile range (IQR)	mean
median	**measure**	measure of central tendency
population	**protractor**	**obtuse angle**
outlier	quartile	**straight angle**
random sample	**ray**	**representative sample**
right angle	**supplementary angles**	vertex
vertical angles	**voluntary response sample**	

Answers and Support for Closure Problems
What Have I Learned?

Problem	Solution		Need Help?	More Practice
CL 8-110.	a. 34	b. $\frac{22}{3}$ or $7\frac{1}{3}$	Lessons 1.2.6, 2.2.5, 2.2.6, and Sections 3.1 and 3.2	Problems CL 4-126, CL 5-155, CL 6-138, 8-9, 8-37, 8-48, 8-62, and 8-107
	c. 0.02	d. $\frac{32}{15}$ or $2\frac{2}{15}$		
	e. −12	f. 70		
			MN: 2.2.5, 2.3.1, 3.1.2, 3.2.2, and 3.2.4	
			LL: 1.2.8, 3.1.1, 3.1.2, 3.2.2, and 3.2.3	

Problem	Solution	Need Help?	More Practice
CL 8-111.	a. $x = 51°$, $2x = 102°$ b. $a = 142°$, $t = 38°$, $c = 38°$	Lessons 8.3.2, 8.3.3, and 8.3.4 MN: 8.3.1 and 8.3.2 LL: 8.3.1	Problems 8-60, 8-75, 8-90, 8-98, and 8-106
CL 8-112.	a. $x + x + x + 9 = 30$; $x = 7$ b. $x° + x° + 23° = 43°$; $x = 10°$	Lessons 2.2.1 and 2.2.2 MN: 3.2.1	Problems CL 3-134, 8-61, and 8-74
CL 8-113.	$x = \frac{35}{22} \approx 1.59$	Section 7.2 MN: 7.2.2 LL: 7.2.2	Problems 7-100, 7-112, and 8-49 (c)
CL 8-114.	114	Lesson 7.1.7 MN: 7.1.7	Problems CL 7-120, 8-16, and 8-36
CL 8-115.	Annika is saving at a faster rate because she saves $75 a week and Eva saves about $71 a week.	Lesson 4.2.3 MN: 4.2.4	Problems CL 7-122, 8-12, and 8-26
CL 8-116.	Each girl started with $7.50.	Section 5.3 MN: 5.3.3 LL: 5.3.4	Problems CL 5-105, CL7-124, 8-11, 8-27, 8-47, and 8-79
CL 8-117.	a. No; the study did not include women. b. No; the study did not include men of all ages and professions. c. No; the study did not include men of all professions. d. This is probably a reasonable conclusion. e. No; we do not know if there are any other side effects.	Section 8.2 MN: 8.2.1 and 8.2.2 LL: 8.2.2	Problems 8-32, 8-35, and 8-45

Circles and Volume

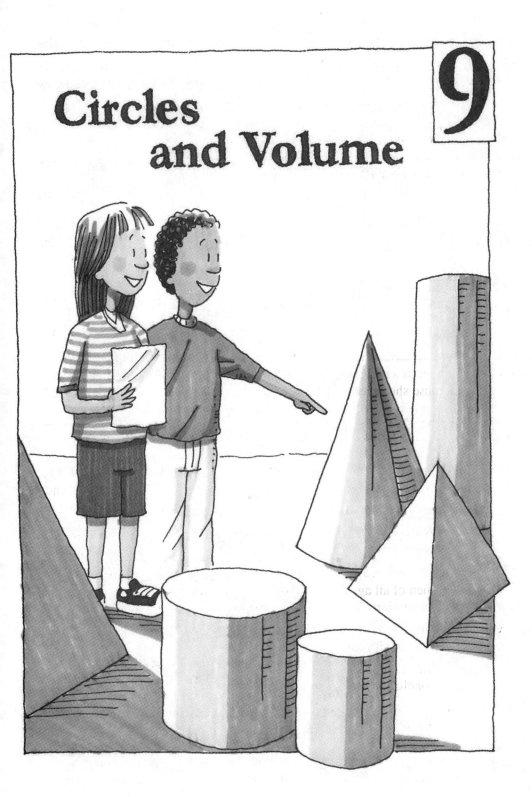

CHAPTER 9   Circles and Volume

Congratulations! You have made it to the last chapter in your math book! Now you will return to geometry, learning how to find the circumference and area of a circle. In Section 9.1, you will also use this concept to find the areas of complicated figures.

In Section 9.2, you will explore how to measure the surface areas and volumes of three-dimensional solids by designing and building cereal boxes. You will visualize what the cut surface of a solid will look like if you slice it at different angles. Finally, you will investigate the volumes of shapes that do not have rectangular bases.

In the course closure and reflection (Section 9.3), you will work with your team to solve challenging problems that allow you to reflect about your learning throughout the course.

Guiding Questions

Think about these questions throughout this chapter:

How are the parts of a circle related?

How can I break this apart?

How much will it hold?

Am I measuring in one, two, or three dimensions?

In this chapter, you will learn how to:

> Calculate the circumferences and areas of circles.
> Find the areas of shapes made up of special quadrilaterals, circles, and triangles.
> Calculate the volumes of some three-dimensional shapes.
> Find the surface areas and volumes of rectangular prisms.

Chapter Outline

Section 9.1	In this section, you will learn about the relationship between the diameter and the circumference of a circle. You will also learn how to calculate the area of a circle from its radius or diameter.
Section 9.2	You will compare how surface area and volume are related by building three-dimensional rectangular prisms. Then you will visualize the shapes made when you slice prisms and use nets to see the surfaces of a prism.
Course Closure and Reflection (Section 9.3)	You will work with your team to solve challenging problems using your learning from the entire course. You will reflect about your learning and how you have been thinking as you have solved problems this year.

9.1.1 What is the multiplier?

Circumference, Diameter, and Pi

You have found *many* proportional relationships in this course. Did you realize that they were so numerous? In future math courses, you will discover that there are other types of relationships that are *not* proportional. Today, however, you will investigate one more, very important proportional relationship: the ratio of the circumference of a circle to its diameter.

9-1.   Imagine a regularly sized can of tennis balls. If you were to wrap a string around the can and cut it so that it does not overlap, and then stretch the same piece of string along the can's length, how would the length of string compare to the length of the can? Would it be shorter than the can? Longer? The same length? Discuss this with your team and make a prediction.*

9-2.   BUBBLE MADNESS

The idea of the **circumference** of a circle is similar to the idea of the perimeter for other shapes; it is the distance around the circle. Wrapping a string around a circular object is one way to measure its circumference. In this activity, you will investigate the relationship of the circumference of a circle to its **diameter**. The diameter is the length from one side of the circle to the other, through its center.

a. Follow the directions below.

- Obtain a bubble wand, some bubble solution, and construction paper from your teacher.

- Blow a bubble and allow it to land and pop on your construction paper. You will see a circle on your paper. (If this does not produce a clear circle, try catching the bubble you blow with your bubble wand and then placing it on the construction paper.)

Problem continues on next page. →

---

* This problem is adapted from the work of Marilyn Burns.
Chapter 9: Circles and Volume

489

9-2.   *Problem continued from previous page.*

- Wrap a string carefully around this circle and then stretch it along a meter stick to measure the **circumference** of the circle. Make your measurement accurate to the nearest tenth of a centimeter.

- Then use a string and ruler to find the longest measurement across the circle (also accurate to the nearest tenth of a centimeter). This is the **diameter**.

Share tasks so that each person has a chance to blow some bubbles and to measure their circumference and diameter. Take data for at least 8 circles of different sizes.

b. Organize your data in a table and then work with your team to decide on an appropriate scale to graph the data carefully on graph paper.

9-3.   WHAT DOES MY GRAPH SHOW?

Discuss the following questions with your team and be prepared to explain your ideas to the class.

a. How can you use your graph to show that the circumference and diameter are related proportionally? (Remember that these are measurements and will thus have some degree of error.)

b. Approximately what is the multiplier between the diameter and the circumference?

9-4.   If the diameter of a bubble were 9 cm, predict its approximate circumference without measuring it. Justify your answer in as many ways as you can.

9-5.   The ratio of circumference to diameter for circles has been measured with increasing accuracy since before 1650 B.C. The ratio has been found to be equal to π. In English, π is spelled *pi* and is pronounced "pie." It is an **irrational number**, which means that there is no way to write it as a fraction with integers. The value of π is slightly greater than 3. Find the button marked "π" on your calculator.

a. Write down the decimal equivalent for π, accurate to the nearest hundredth.

b. The fraction $\frac{22}{7}$ is often used to approximate π. What is the decimal equivalent of $\frac{22}{7}$, accurate to the nearest hundredth?

9-6.   Work with your team to generalize the relationship between circumference and diameter of a circle. In other words, describe how you could calculate the circumference of any circle if you knew the diameter, and how you could find the length of the diameter if you knew the circumference.

9-7.   Now return to your prediction from problem 9-1. Discuss it with your team again. Has your prediction changed? Why or why not? Work with your team to test your prediction.

9-8.   Scientists have measured the diameter of the earth at the equator to be about 7926 miles.

    a.   If you were to travel all the way around the earth along the equator, approximately how many miles would you have traveled?

    b.   **Additional Challenge 1:** If it takes the average human two hours to walk five miles, how long would it take a person to walk around the earth, assuming it is actually possible to do so?

    c.   **Additional Challenge 2:** Signals that travel across the Internet are often carried through fiber-optic cables and travel at the speed of light, approximately 186,000 miles every second. At this rate, how long would it take an e-mail to travel around the earth?

9-9.   LEARNING LOG

Write a Learning Log entry summarizing what you learned about circumference and its relationship to the diameter of a circle. Title this entry "Circumference and Diameter" and label it with today's date.

9-10.   Estimate the circumference or diameter for each of the following circles. For each one, give your reasoning.

    a.   The diameter is 1 cm. What is the circumference?

    b.   The diameter is 7.2 meters. What is the circumference?

    c.   The circumference is 1 mile. What is the diameter?

    d.   The circumference is 12 inches. What is the diameter?

9-11.   Imagine that you and your team will be conducting a survey to see how many minutes long lunch should be at your school. Students understand that the longer lunch is, the longer the school day is. Since you cannot ask every student, you will take a sample.

  a. You ask every tenth student leaving a school-wide assembly to stop and think about how long he or she would like lunch to be. Do you think this sample is representative of the whole school?

  b. These are the answers, in minutes, from the first 20 students:

    60 40 50 25 30 15 30 50 50 35 45 25 25 50 25 60 55 60 60 15

    Make an inference (a statistical prediction) about the average length *all* students at your school think lunch should be.

9-12.   Sasha saved $850 from her summer job last summer. She put it in an account that earns simple interest each month. After 9 months, her account is worth $1003. What percent interest did she earn each month?

9-13.   Copy the axes below and complete the scales.

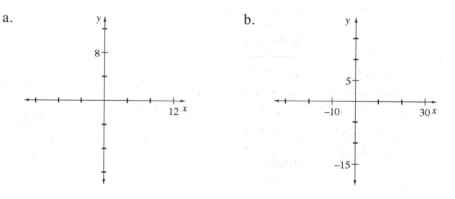

9-14.   Janet sells erasers at a price of 8 erasers for 60 cents. She started this table to show the price for different numbers of erasers.

Erasers	8	4	1	12	10	16	100
$	0.60						

  a. Complete her table.

  b. Does this situation represent a proportional relationship? Why or why not?

  c. Use the information in the table to find the cost of 144 erasers. Write and solve a proportion, if appropriate.

9-15.   Jack has 120 songs on his music player. Some are rock, some are jazz, and the rest are classical pieces. If his music player is on random shuffle mode, the probability that it will play a classical piece is $\frac{2}{5}$ and the probability that it will play a jazz piece is $\frac{1}{3}$. How many songs of each type are on Jack's music player?

9-16.   Find the circumference of each of the circles described below.

a.   Radius of 3 inches   b.   Diameter of 27 cm

9-17.   The table below shows a list of sampling methods. From what populations are these samples taken? Write down the actual population for each of these sampling techniques.

Method of Sampling	Description of Actual Population
Call every hundredth name in the phone book.	People with phones who have their number listed.
Call people at home at 10 a.m.	
Ask every tenth person who leaves the mall.	
Ask people leaving the bank.	
Mail questionnaires to people.	
Ask everyone on the school bus.	

9-18.   A pair of shoes originally costs $42 but is on sale for 33% off. What is the new price? Show how you know.

9-19.   The students at Dolan Middle School are competing in after-school activities in which they earn points for helping out around the school. Each team consists of the 30 students in a homeroom. Halfway through the competition, the scores from the students in two of the teams were displayed in the plots at right.

The champion team is the one with the most points when the scores of the 30 students on the team are added. Which team would you rather be on? Explain.

9-20.   Copy each problem. Then find the sum, difference, product, or quotient. Remember to show all of your steps.

a. $23.6 + 12$

b. $16.5 + 52.43$

c. $46.21 - 31.2$

d. $27.5 - 13.11$

e. $4.5(6)$

f. $55 \div 2$

9-21.   Review the definitions of complementary, supplementary, and vertical angles. Use the information to answer the following questions.

a.   Two angles are complementary. If one measures $65°$, what is the measure of the other angle?

b.   Two angles are supplementary. If one measures $125°$, what is the measure of the other angle?

c.   Two angles are vertical. If one measures $63°$, what is the measure of the other angle?

9.1.2 How can I measure the area?

Area of Circles

The ratio known as π (*pi*, prounounced "pie") was first discovered by the Babylonians nearly 4000 years ago. Over the years, Egyptian, Chinese, and Greek mathematicians also found the constant ratio between the circumference and diameter of a circle by using measurement. The Greek letter π has been used to represent this ratio since the 1700s when it was made popular by the Swiss mathematician Euler (pronounced "oy-ler"). Even though this ratio has been known for many years, the value commonly used for π is still only an approximation.

9-22.　ESTIMATING CIRCLE AREA

A circle is different from any shape you have studied so far because it has no sides or corners. This makes it difficult to apply the strategy of decomposing it into rectangles and triangles to find its area. In this situation, estimating its area can be a useful technique. Obtain a Lesson 9.1.2A Resource Page from your teacher.

a. Using the first circle with a **radius** (distance from the center to the circle) of 5 units on the resource page, estimate the area of the circle by counting whole and part squares. When each person in your team has finished his or her own estimate, share your results.

b. Are all of the estimates in your team identical? How can you combine your data as a team to get a new estimate that may be more accurate?

9-23.　THE INSIDE OUTSIDE AVERAGE METHOD

While it is convenient to estimate area when shapes are drawn on grid paper, shapes are often not presented in that way. How can other shapes be used to help estimate area? Look carefully at the shape at right (also shown on the resource page).

a. How can you find the area of the larger square? What is the area of the larger square?

b. How can you find the area of the smaller square? What is the area of the smaller square?

c. How does the actual area of the circle compare to the area of each square? Is either square a good estimate of the circle's area? Why or why not?

d. Discuss with your team how to use the areas of both the squares to estimate the area of the circle. You might consider using what you have learned about analyzing data. Explain your thinking.

9-24.   Julia needs to estimate the area of a circle with a radius of 6 grid units. She decides to use the Inside Outside Average method to make her estimate.

a.   On the Lesson 9.1.2A Resource Page, estimate the area of the circle with a radius of 6 grid units by counting whole squares and parts of squares. Share your results with your team.

b.   When Julia was calculating the area of the outside square, she started by dividing the large square into four smaller ones. Her picture is at right.

To find the area of each small square, Julia multiplied the length times the width:

$$\text{Area} = 6^2 = 36 \text{ sq. grid units}$$

How are the length, width, and area of each small square related to the radius of the circle? How is the area of the outside square related to the radius?

c.   Julia divided the inside square into triangles. How is each triangle related to the radius? How is the area of the inside square related to the radius?

d.   If the area of the two squares is related to the radius of the circle, Julia wonders if she can relate her circle estimate back to the radius as well. With your team, look at the estimate for area you have from part (a). How is that area estimate related to the radius of the circle?

9-25.   Julia is looking at a new circle with a radius of 10 grid units. So far on her paper, she has written the work at right. What expression should she write to estimate the area of the circle?

$$\text{Outside area} = 4(10)^2$$
$$\text{Inside area} = 2(10)^2$$

9-26.   A FORMULA FOR CIRCLE AREA

By using the Inside Outside Average method for estimating, you discovered that the area of a circle is approximately three times the radius squared. There is another way to decompose and rearrange a circle in order to find a formula for its area. As you go through this process, think about these questions:

- *If a circle is cut up and rearranged into a new shape, is the area of the new shape the same as the area of the circle?*

- *How are the dimensions (base and height) of the new shape related to the circle?*

- *Would this process work for any circle? Does it matter how large the circle is?*

Problem continues on next page. →

9-26. *Problem continued from previous page.*

Take a circle and cut it into 8 equal parts and arrange them like this:

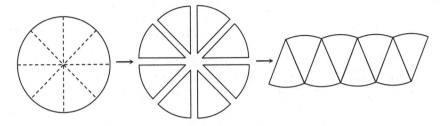

This rearrangement of the circle would look even more like a parallelogram or rectangle if you cut the circle into more pieces:

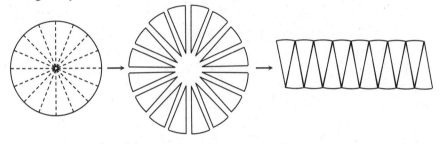

The measurements of this parallelogram are actually related to the original measurements of the circle. The height of the parallelogram is the same as the radius of the circle:

The length of the parallelogram is approximately half of the circumference of the circle. Since the circumference is equal to πd, half of the circumference is equal to:

$$\frac{\pi d}{2} = \frac{\pi(2r)}{2} = \pi r .$$

Substituting these values into the formula for the area of a parallelogram, you get:

$$A = hb = r(\pi r) = r^2\pi .$$

9-27. Calculate the area for the circles with radii (plural of radius) of 5 and 6 grid units using this new method (the formula $A = r^2\pi$) and compare your answers to your team's estimates in problems 9-23 and 9-24. How are the areas using this new method different from the estimates in the Inside Outside Average Method?

9-28.   How does the area that you found in problem 9-22 (counting estimate) compare to the calculating the area of a circle with a radius of 5 grid units using the formula
$A = r^2\pi$?

9-29.   **Additional Challenge:** A circle with radius 6 inches is cut into four quarters. Those pieces are rearranged into the shape at right. Find the area and the perimeter of the shape.

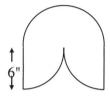

9-30.   LEARNING LOG

Write a Learning Log entry that explains how to use the formula for the area of a circle. Include a solved example problem. Title this entry "Area of Circles" and include today's date.

METHODS AND MEANINGS

Circumference and Area of Circles

MATH NOTES

The **circumference** (C) of a circle is its perimeter, that is, the "distance around" the circle.

The number π (read "pi") is the ratio of the circumference of a circle to its diameter. That is, $\pi = \frac{\text{circumference}}{\text{diameter}}$. This definition is also used as a way of computing the circumference of a circle if you know the diameter as in the formula $C = \pi d$ where C is the circumference and d is the diameter. Since the diameter is twice the radius (that is, $d = 2r$) the formula for the circumference of a circle using its radius is $C = \pi(2r)$ or $C = 2\pi \cdot r$.

$C = \pi \cdot d$

The first few digits of π are 3.141592.

To find the **area** (A) of a circle when given its radius (r), square the radius and multiply by π. This formula can be written as $A = r^2 \cdot \pi$. Another way the area formula is often written is $A = \pi \cdot r^2$.

9-31.   The circle shown at right has a diameter of 20 cm.

a.   What measurement do you need to find in order to
calculate the area inside the circle?

b.   Find the area inside the circle using the formula $A = r^2\pi$. Write your
answer as a product of r^2 and π, and as an approximation using $\pi \approx 3.14$.

9-32.   Find the area and circumference of the circles in parts (a) and (b) and the radius
in part (c). You may want to refer to the Math Notes box in this lesson.

a.   b.   c. $C = 314\,\text{cm}$

15 m   9 in

9-33.   Use a ruler and a protractor to construct a triangle with two sides of 4 cm and
5.2 cm and an angle measuring 45°.

9-34.   For each diagram below, identify each set of angles as complementary,
supplementary, or vertical. Then use what you know about the properties of
angles to find the measure of each angle labeled with a variable.

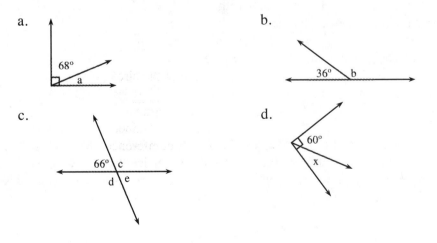

a.   b.

68°   36°   b
a

c.   d.

66° c   60°
d e   x

9-35.   The Shones' family orchard produces 130 pounds of fruit per tree using traditional farming techniques. They would like to change to biodynamic farming techniques that will increase their crop by 20%. Changing techniques will cost money, but the fruit crop will be larger. Help them decide if they should change by calculating how much they will be able to grow two different ways, using two different scale factors (one multiplier will be greater than one). How many more pounds of fruit per tree will they get?

9-36.   Howie and Steve are making cookies for themselves and some friends. The recipe they are using will make 48 cookies, but they only want to make 16 cookies. They have no trouble reducing the amounts of flour and sugar, but the original recipe calls for $1\frac{3}{4}$ cups of butter. Help Howie and Steve determine how much butter they will need.

9-37.   Jessica's parents are planning their new house. They received a scale drawing from an architect, and Jessica is trying to figure out how big her bedroom will be. The architect has noted that each $\frac{1}{4}$ inch on his drawing represents one foot of distance in the new house. If the diagram of Jessica's room measures $2\frac{1}{2}$ inches by $4\frac{1}{4}$ inches, what will be the actual dimensions of her new room?

9-38.   Stuart is a plumber working on the Garcia family's house. He is working with PVC pipe that has an internal diameter of $\frac{3}{4}$ inch. The thickness of the pipe is $\frac{3}{16}$ inch. What is the exterior (outside) diameter of the pipe?

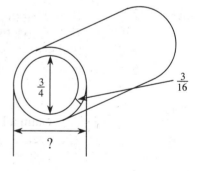

9-39.   Quintrell was writing a "Guess My Number" game. He decided to write the clues in a different way. He wrote, *"When 35 is added to my number, the answer is 4 times my original number plus 8. What is my number?"* Use the 5-D Process to find Quintrell's number.

9-40.   If m and n are integers, which fractions below are equivalent?

   a. $\frac{-m}{n}$ b. $-\frac{m}{n}$ c. $\frac{-m}{-n}$ d. $\frac{m}{-n}$ e. $\frac{m}{n}$

9-41.   Thu has a bag with 7 green marbles, 5 blue marbles, and 4 red marbles. For
         each part below, if the marble selected is replaced before the next marble is
         drawn, what is the probability that she will draw:

         a. A red marble?   b. A red or a green marble?   c. An orange marble?

9.1.3 What is the area?

Area of Composite Shapes

In this lesson, you will consolidate your understanding of area as you find areas of
complicated shapes. As you work on the problems in this lesson, ask your team members
these questions:

> How can we break this up into shapes that we can find the areas of?

> Is there another way to see it?

> Can we see the total area as a sum of areas? As a difference of areas?

9-42.   Shakira is planning to put a lawn in her backyard by installing sod (rolls of
         grass) and needs to know how many square feet of sod she should order. Her
         yard is irregularly shaped and has a fishpond in the center. The dimensions of
         the lawn she is planning are shaded in the diagram below. All measurements
         are in feet.

         Your Task: Obtain a Lesson 9.1.3A Resource Page from your teacher and
         work with your team to make a recommendation for how much sod Shakira
         should order. Can you find more than one way to calculate the area of
         Shakira's lawn?

9-43.   Find the area of the part of a typical basketball court shaded in the diagram at right.

9-44.   Gina designs and makes her own clothes. She drew the diagram at right (and also on the Lesson 9.1.3B Resource Page) of the fabric she needs for the front and back of a new shirt. If each unit on the grid represents one inch, how much fabric will she need?

══════ Review & Preview ══════

9-45.   The shape at right is composed of a rectangle and a semi-circle (half of a circle).

a.   Find the perimeter.

b.   Find the area.

9-46.   Draw a parallelogram with a base of 3 cm and a height of 7 cm and show how to calculate its area.

9-47.   Find the areas of the circles with dimensions given below.

a.   Radius: 4 ft   b.   Diameter: 0.6 cm

9-48.   Leonard has purchased packages of grid paper for $2.25. If he wants to make a 40% profit on each package he sells to his classmates, by how much should he increase the price? What will the new price be?

9-49. Simplify these expressions.

a. $(x+3.5)2$ b. $23+5x-(7+2.5x)$ c. $3x+4.4-2(6.6+x)$

9-50. Two employees of Frontier Fence Company can install 100 feet of fence in two days.

a. What is the unit rate for one employee?

b. Write a proportion to show the relationship between this rate and 150 feet of fence.

c. At this same rate, how many employees are needed to install 150 feet of fence in one day?

9.2.1 Does surface area affect volume?

Surface Area and Volume

In your work with two-dimensional (flat) shapes, you have described their dimensions, their perimeters, and their areas. For three-dimensional shapes — shapes that have length, width, *and* depth — you can measure the lengths of their edges and calculate the areas of their faces (sides). Three-dimensional shapes can also be described by their volumes, or how much space they enclose. Today you will work with rectangle-based prisms. As you work, keep these questions in mind:

How many cubes would it take to fill it?

How many squares would it take to cover the outside of it?

9-51.   PERFECT PACKAGING

Cereal boxes come in different shapes and sizes.
Some are tall and skinny, while others are shorter
or deeper. The Bravo Breakfast cereal company is
considering changing the size of its box. The staff
members need some data to help them make the
best choice.

The company currently packages its Morning Math Crunch cereal in a box that
is 2" deep by 4" wide by 8" tall, as pictured at right. This shape is called a **right
rectangular prism** because the top and bottom faces are rectangles that are
congruent (same size and shape) and parallel to each other. These are called the
bases. The other faces (sides of the box) are also rectangles that are
perpendicular (at a right angle) to the bases. Use a set of cubes to build a model
of this box. Assume that the edge of one cube represents 1" of length on the
real cereal box.

a.   Describe the box as completely as you can. Include the information below.

   • What shapes do you see when you look at the faces of the box?

   • What lengths or other measurements can you describe?

   • Sketch each shape on your paper, and label it completely.

b.   The cardboard sides of the box are called its **faces**. How much cardboard is
needed to create all six of the faces of the box? Work with your team to
develop a method for calculating this amount. Discuss the kind of units to
use. Be ready to explain your method to the class.

c.   The number of square units that it takes to cover the outside of an object,
like the amount of cardboard you found in part (b), is called the object's
surface area. The **volume** of a shape is the measure of how much it will
hold. Volume is measured in cubic units.

   How many cubes did you use to make this model of the cereal box? How
many cubic inches of cereal will the box hold?

Core Connections, Course 2

9-52. The waste-management division at Bravo Breakfast is worried that the box for Morning Math Crunch uses too much cardboard. The waste-management crew wants to make a box that holds the same amount of cereal but uses less cardboard.

   a. What measurement of the box is the waste-management division interested in **minimizing** (making as small as possible)? What measurement does the company want to keep the same? What could change?

   b. With your team, use the cubes to build different rectangular prisms that will still hold 64 cubic inches of cereal. Each box must be a rectangular prism with exactly six faces. For each prism you create:

   - Sketch the prism,

   - Label the dimensions on your sketch, and

   - Find the surface area.

   How many different prisms can you make?

   c. Do all of the prisms you built have the same volume? How do you know?

   d. Which box will use the smallest amount of cardboard?

9-53. Use cubes to build each prism below. Find the surface area and volume of each shape.

   a.   b.

   c. Use at least 15 cubes to build a prism of your own design. Sketch the prism and find its surface area and volume.

9-54. LEARNING LOG

   Write step-by-step directions explaining to another student how to find the surface area of a prism. You may want to use one of the prisms in problem 9-53 as an example. Give reasons for each step. Record your directions in your Learning Log. Title the entry "Surface Area of a Prism" and label it with today's date.

METHODS AND MEANINGS

Polygons, Prisms, and Pyramids

A **polygon** is a two-dimensional closed figure made of straight-line segments connected end to end. The segments may not cross. The point where two sides meet is called a **vertex** (plural: vertices). Polygons are named by the number of sides they have. Polygons with three through ten sides are named and illustrated below.

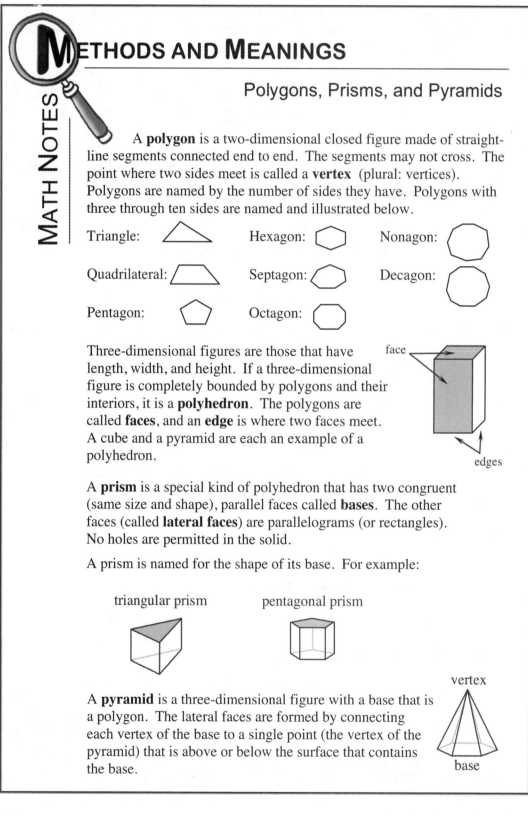

Triangle:

Quadrilateral:

Pentagon:

Hexagon:

Septagon:

Octagon:

Nonagon:

Decagon:

Three-dimensional figures are those that have length, width, and height. If a three-dimensional figure is completely bounded by polygons and their interiors, it is a **polyhedron**. The polygons are called **faces**, and an **edge** is where two faces meet. A cube and a pyramid are each an example of a polyhedron.

face

edges

A **prism** is a special kind of polyhedron that has two congruent (same size and shape), parallel faces called **bases**. The other faces (called **lateral faces**) are parallelograms (or rectangles). No holes are permitted in the solid.

A prism is named for the shape of its base. For example:

triangular prism

pentagonal prism

A **pyramid** is a three-dimensional figure with a base that is a polygon. The lateral faces are formed by connecting each vertex of the base to a single point (the vertex of the pyramid) that is above or below the surface that contains the base.

vertex

base

9-55.   Read the Math Notes box in this lesson. Use the information to determine whether each shape below is a polygon.

a.   b.   c.   d.

9-56.   Find the volume and surface area of each shape below. Assume that the edge of each cube measures 1".

a.   b.   c.

9-57.   Red apples cost $1.20 per pound, and green apples cost $1.50 per pound.

a.   Write an expression to represent the total cost of x pounds of red apples and y pounds of green apples.

b.   What is the total cost if you buy 3 pounds of red apples and 2 pounds of green apples?

9-58.   Ellen is building a scale model of the space shuttle. A space shuttle is approximately 122 feet long and has a wingspan of 78 feet.

a.   How many inches long is the space shuttle?

b.   Ellen plans to build her model so that 1 cm on the model represents 10 inches on the space shuttle. Write a proportion to show this relationship for the length of her model. Find how long will her model be (in centimeters)?

c.   Write and solve a proportion to find her model's wingspan (in centimeters).

d.   Remember that 1 inch is approximately equal to 2.54 cm. How many inches long will her model be?

9-59.   Find the area and circumference of a circle with a radius of 7 cm.

9-60.   Find the area and perimeter of each shape below. Show your steps and work.

a.   All angles are right angles.

b.

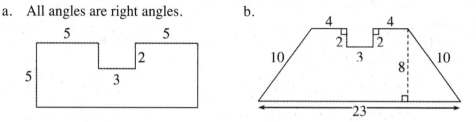

9.2.2 How can I slice it?

Cross Sections

A **cross section** of a three-dimensional solid (an object that has length, width, and height) is the figure obtained when the solid is intersected or "sliced" by a plane (an object that has only length and width, like a flat sheet of paper). Today you will investigate the shapes that can be created by slicing various types of solids.

9-61. Using clay, make a rectangular prism or cube. An example is shown below right. Each person in your team should make a slightly different prism.

a. Use your string to slice the rectangular prism by holding it tightly and pulling it through the solid. An example is shown at right. Place the newly created face made by the slice that came from the inside of the rectangular prism on your paper and trace the resulting shape. What is the name of your shape?

b. Which of the following shapes can you make by slicing your prism in different ways? Before making a new slice, reshape your prism.

   i.   Triangle
   ii.   Square
   iii. Rectangle
   iv.   Trapezoid
   v.   Parallelogram
   vi.   Pentagon
   vii. Hexagon
   viii. Octagon
   ix.   Circle

c. Even though each team member had a slightly different rectangular prism, were you able to create the same cross sections? Were there any shapes that one team member could create and another could not?

9-62.   Now make a rectangular pyramid. An example is
         shown at right. Again, each person in your team
         should make a slightly different pyramid.

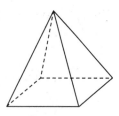

   a.   Use your string as you did in problem 9-61 to
        slice the pyramid. Place the newly created face
        that is made by the slice and came from the inside
        of the pyramid on your paper and trace the
        resulting shape. What is the name of your shape?

   b.   What other shapes can you make by slicing your pyramid in different
        ways? What shapes are impossible to make? How do the types of shapes
        that you can make with the rectangular pyramid compare to the types of
        shapes that you made with the rectangular prism?

9-63.   CROSS SECTIONS AND VOLUME

         In Lesson 9.2.1, you learned that the volume of a solid is found by determining
         the number of cubes it takes to create the solid.

   a.   Make a rectangular prism similar to the one you made in problem 9-61.
        How can you repeatedly slice the prism so that each of the slices that you
        create is the same size and shape? Discuss this with your team and then
        slice your prism into equal pieces.

   b.   Take one of your slices and cut it into cubes of the approximately same
        size. How many cubes are in one slice?

   c.   Using the number of cubes from a single slice of the prism and the number
        of slices you created, how many cubes would it take to build your prism?

   d.   Find the volume of each prism below. Make sure everyone on your team
        agrees with the answers.

Core Connections, Course 2

9-64. Sanne made a prism and sliced it into equally sized pieces as you did in problem 9-63, but she is only letting you see the slice shown at right.

a. Draw a sketch of Sanne's prism.

b. Sanne told you that her prism has 8 slices like this one that are each the same. What is the volume of her prism?

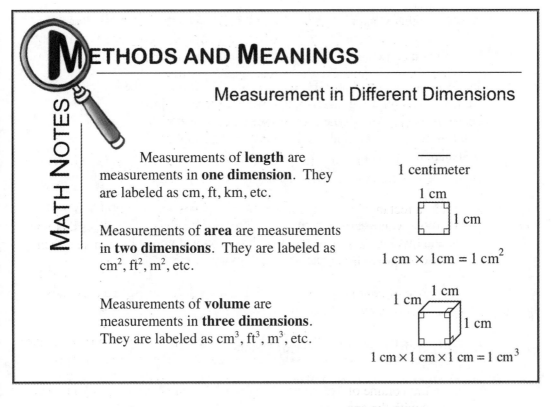

METHODS AND MEANINGS

Measurement in Different Dimensions

MATH NOTES

Measurements of **length** are measurements in **one dimension**. They are labeled as cm, ft, km, etc.

1 centimeter

1 cm

1 cm

Measurements of **area** are measurements in **two dimensions**. They are labeled as cm^2, ft^2, m^2, etc.

$1 \text{ cm} \times 1 \text{cm} = 1 \text{ cm}^2$

Measurements of **volume** are measurements in **three dimensions**. They are labeled as cm^3, ft^3, m^3, etc.

1 cm

1 cm

1 cm

$1 \text{ cm} \times 1 \text{ cm} \times 1 \text{ cm} = 1 \text{ cm}^3$

Review & Preview

9-65. Use the pyramid shown at right to answer the questions below.

a. If the pyramid were sliced vertically, what would the resulting cross sections look like? Sketch them.

b. If the pyramid were sliced horizontally, what would the resulting cross section look like? Sketch it.

9-66.   Use the rectangular prism shown at right to complete parts (a) through (d) below.

4 cm

12 cm

3 cm

a.   Calculate the surface area of the prism. Show all of your subproblems.

b.   Explain why the exponent for area units is 2 (that is, cm²).

c.   Calculate the volume of the prism.

d.   Explain why the exponent for volume units is a 3 (that is, cm³).

9-67.   James lives in Columbus, OH, and wants to know how far he is from Indianapolis. On his map, the two cities are $1\frac{3}{4}$ inches apart. At the bottom of the map, he sees the scale at right. Write a proportion and then find the distance from Columbus to Indianapolis.

$\frac{1}{4}$ inch

25 miles

9-68.   Kenny took some measurements on the front of his house and quickly drew a sketch, which is shown at right. Use his sketch to create a scale drawing of the front of Kenny's house.

45°

12 ft

30.5 ft

9-69.   Simplify each of the following expressions.

a. $3\frac{1}{5}\cdot\frac{7}{4}$

b. $5^3\cdot\left(-\frac{4}{5}\right)$

c. $2^4\cdot\frac{5}{8}$

d. $-\frac{1}{2}\cdot3^2$

e. $-\frac{5}{6}+\left(\frac{1}{2}\right)^2$

f. $\left(-\frac{4}{5}\right)^2-\frac{3}{50}$

g. $\left(\frac{3}{10}\right)^2-\left(-\frac{2}{5}\right)^2$

h. $8^2\left(-\frac{7}{8}\right)-\frac{1}{2}$

9-70.   Evaluate the inequality $x+4<2x-3$ for the following values of x. Decide if the given value of x makes the statement true or false. Show all of your work.

a. $x=4$

b. $x=-2$

c. $x=7$

d. $x=9$

9.2.3 How much will fill it?

Volume of a Prism

You have had a lot of practice with finding the area of flat, two-dimensional shapes. Today you will begin using those skills to help you understand shapes with a third dimension. As you work, consider the following questions.

> How can we see the shape in layers?

> How can we slice the shape so that the layers are identical?

9-71.   BIRTHDAY SWEETS

Laverne is making a birthday dessert for her cousin Leslie. She wants to incorporate Leslie's favorite ingredients: cookies and chocolate mousse. She will make the dessert in a special L-shaped pan that is 9.5 cm deep.

First, Laverne is going to make a cookie crust as the bottom layer. The crust will be 1 cm thick so that it is nice and crunchy. She is going to add chocolate mousse on top of the crust until the mousse is 7 cm thick. Finally, she will add a 1.5-cm layer of whipped cream on the mousse and top it with chocolate sprinkles.

a.   What area will the dessert cover (in square centimeters) on the pan?

b.   Laverne needs to know what quantity of cookies to buy to make the crust layer of the dessert. Does the measurement she needs describe length, area, or volume? Discuss this with your team, and then write down your explanation.

c.   One cookie will crush into about 5 cubic centimeters of cookie crumbs. Show Laverne how to find out how many cookies she will need to make the crust layer. Be sure to explain your reasoning. How many cookies should she buy?

9-72.   Laverne wants the mousse on top of the crust to be 7 cm thick. Use your answer from part (c) of problem 9-71 to help you figure out how many cubic centimeters of mousse Laverne will need. Explain your reasoning.

9-73.   Laverne has 1200 cubic centimeters of whipped cream ready to spread on top of the mousse. Erika looked at Laverne's notes about how much cream she would need and exclaimed, *"You have too much! You will overflow the pan!"*

How could Erika know that Laverne has too much whipped cream? Be prepared to share your ideas with the class. Determine how much extra or how short Laverne is of the amount of whipped cream that she needs.

9-74.   Laverne needs to be sure that her finished dessert will be enough to serve everyone.

   a.   What is the total volume of dessert that Laverne is planning to make? Be ready to share your study team's strategy with the class.

   b.   If one serving is 285 cm^3, how many people will the dessert serve?

9-75.   For the prism at right, find the volume of a layer 1 cm high. Then, find the total volume of the prism. Every face is a rectangle.

5 cm
6 cm
22 cm

9-76.   **Additional Challenge:** When finding the volume of the shape below, Audrey found the volume of the shaded layer first. Here is her work:

$$5 + 20 = 25 \text{, so } 25 \cdot 8 = 200 \text{ ft}^3$$

Then she said, *"The shape is 22 feet high, so there are 22 one-foot-high layers."* She then multiplied and got this answer:

$$22 \cdot 200 = 4400 \text{ ft}^3$$

a.   What was Audrey's mistake?

b.   What is the actual volume of the shape? Explain how you found it.

Review & Preview

9-77.   Find the surface area and volume of the prism shown at right.

9-78.   Find the area of each circle below.

a.   radius = 8 cm

b.   60 cm

9-79.   Glenda made a scale model of the Empire State Building in New York. The building itself is 1250 feet high, and her scale model is 5 feet high.

a.   Write a ratio that compares the heights of the two buildings.

b.   If the doorway of Glenda's model is 2 inches wide, how wide would you expect the doorway of the real building to be? Write and solve a proportion.

c.   If the real building contains 102 floors, how many floors should Glenda's model contain?

9-80.   Simplify each of the following expressions.

a. $8^2 + 7^2$

b. $7^2 \cdot 7 \cdot 7$

c. $\left(\frac{1}{2}\right)^2 + \left(\frac{2}{3}\right)^2$

d. $(2^2 + 6)^2$

e. $-4 \cdot 3^2 - 2$

f. $x - x$

g. $3 \cdot 3 \div 3$

h. $4x + x - 2x$

i. $-2 \cdot 4 \div 4$

9-81.   The Wild West Frontier Park now offers an unlimited day pass. For $29.00, visitors can go on as many rides as they want. The original plan charged visitors $8.75 to enter the park plus $2.25 for each ride. Write an equation to determine the number of rides that would make the total cost equal for the two plans. Solve the equation.

9-82.   Do girls read more than boys during the summer? Serena's class asked 30 parents to estimate how many pages their child read over the summer. They collected the following data.

Girls: 10 30 230 130 110 240 150 260 60 230 100 20 50 160 90 pages

Boys: 210 100 0 40 260 240 200 220 190 150 50 100 12 140 40 pages

a. Make parallel box plots and compare the center, shape, spread, and outliers.

b. Do girls read more? How many IQRs more do they read? Use the box plots to estimate.

9.2.4 How much will it hold?

Volume of Non-Rectangular Prisms

In this lesson, you will investigate different strategies for finding the volume of non-rectangular prisms. The problems require you to describe how you visualize each shape. As you work with your team, ask each other these questions to focus your discussion:

How can the shape be broken down into simpler shapes?

Can we break the shape into equal layers or slices?

9-83.   THE SHELL BOX

Laurel keeps her seashell collection in a small box that is shaped like a rectangular prism with a base of 4" by 3" and height of 5" (see diagram at right). She wants to make a bigger box for her shells, and she has found a pattern that she likes. The pattern has two sides that are pentagons, and the finished box will look like a miniature house (see picture at right). Use the net on the Lesson 9.2.4 Resource Page to construct a paper model of Laurel's new box.

a. Calculate the volume of Laurel's original small box. What method did you use?

b. Laurel was trying to figure out the volume of the new box.

One of her friends said, *"Why don't you find the volume of one layer and then figure out how many layers there would be?"*

Another friend said, *"What if you separated the pentagon into two parts, so that you have a rectangular prism and a prism with a triangle base? Then you could find the volume of the two parts separately and put them back together."*

Talk about each of these strategies with your team. Could Laurel use these ideas to find the volume of her new box?

c. Work with your team to calculate the volume of Laurel's new box. Show your thinking clearly and be prepared to share your method with the class.

9-84.   Find the volume of the prism at right
         using any method you choose. Be
         prepared to explain your reasoning.

9-85.   Bryan was looking at the prism in problem 9-84 with his team. He wondered
         how they could slice the prism horizontally into layers that would all be the
         same size.

    a.   If the team slices the shape so that the bottom layer has the 10 ft by 38 ft
         rectangle as its base, will each layer be equal in size?

    b.   How could the team turn or tip the shape so that if the shape is sitting on a
         table and is cut horizontally, each layer will be the same size and shape?
         Which face will rest on the table?

    c.   When does it make sense to tip the shape in order to see the layers?
         Discuss this question with your team and summarize your conclusion on
         your paper.

9-86.   LEARNING LOG

         The method for finding the volume of a prism is commonly
         described as "finding the area of the base, then multiplying
         by the height." Discuss with your study team how this
         strategy works. How does the area of the base help to find the volume? Does it
         matter which face is the base? Why do you multiply by the height? Record
         your conclusions in your Learning Log. Title the entry, "Volume of a Prism,"
         and label it with today's date.

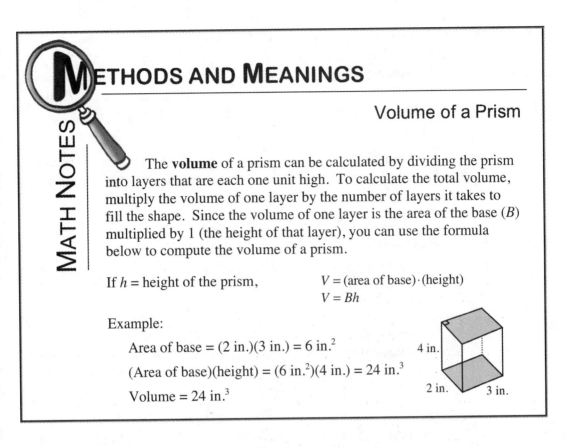

METHODS AND MEANINGS

MATH NOTES

Volume of a Prism

The **volume** of a prism can be calculated by dividing the prism into layers that are each one unit high. To calculate the total volume, multiply the volume of one layer by the number of layers it takes to fill the shape. Since the volume of one layer is the area of the base (B) multiplied by 1 (the height of that layer), you can use the formula below to compute the volume of a prism.

If h = height of the prism,
$$V = (\text{area of base}) \cdot (\text{height})$$
$$V = Bh$$

Example:

Area of base = $(2 \text{ in.})(3 \text{ in.}) = 6 \text{ in.}^2$

(Area of base)(height) = $(6 \text{ in.}^2)(4 \text{ in.}) = 24 \text{ in.}^3$

Volume = 24 in.^3

4 in.

2 in.   3 in.

Review & Preview

9-87. Is each shape below a prism? If so, identify the shape that is the base. If not, explain why not.

a. b. c. d.

9-88. Find the volume of a 1-unit-high layer of each prism below. Then find the total volume and the surface area of each figure.

a.   A rectangular prism

10 m

10 m

50 m

b.   A triangle-based prism

12.7 cm

8 cm

9 cm   9 cm

9-89.   Use the prism shown at right to answer the questions below.

   a. If the prism were sliced vertically, sketch the resulting
       cross section.

   b. If the prism were sliced horizontally, sketch the resulting
       cross section.

9-90.   Find the area and circumference of a circle that has a diameter of 17 mm. Write
         your answers in terms of π and as a decimal approximation.

9-91.   A bag of marbles contains only the colors red and green.

   a. If the probability of getting a red marble is $\frac{1}{3}$, what is the probability of
       getting a green marble?

   b. If there are 24 marbles in the bag, how many are green?

   c. What is the probability of drawing two marbles that are red? Note: The
       first marble is not replaced before drawing the second. Write your answer
       as a fraction and as a percent.

   d. What is the probability of drawing two red marbles if the first one is
       replaced before the second one is drawn? Write your answer as a fraction
       and as a percent.

9-92.   This problem is a checkpoint for unit rates and proportions. It will be referred
         to as Checkpoint 9.

         In parts (a) and (b), compute the unit rate. In parts (c) and (d), solve the
         proportion.

   a. Tina drove 108 miles and used 4.5 gallons of gasoline. Compute the miles
       per gallon.

   b. If 17 oranges cost $3.23, compute the cost per orange.

   c. $\frac{x}{12} = \frac{20}{30}$ d. $\frac{13}{40} = \frac{m}{100}$

         Check your answers by referring to the Checkpoint 9 materials located at the
         back of your book.

         Ideally, at this point you are comfortable working with these types of problems
         and can solve them correctly. If you feel that you need more confidence when
         solving these types of problems, then review the Checkpoint 9 materials and try
         the practice problems provided. From this point on, you will be expected to do
         problems like these correctly and with confidence.

520

Chapter 9 Closure   What have I learned?

Reflection and Synthesis

The activities below offer you a chance to reflect
about what you have learned during this chapter.
As you work, look for concepts that you feel very
comfortable with, ideas that you would like to learn
more about, and topics you need more help with.

①   WHAT HAVE I LEARNED?

Doing the problems in this section will help you to evaluate which types of
problems you feel comfortable with and which ones you need more help with.

Solve each problem as completely as you can. The table at the end of this
closure section provides answers to these problems. It also tells you where you
can find additional help and where to find practice problems like them.

CL 9-93.   Find the area and circumference of a circle with a radius of 6.5 cm.

CL 9-94.   Find the surface area and volume of each solid below.

    a.   All angles are right angles.   b.   Right prism with base area = 48 cm²

CL 9-95.   Find the surface area and volume of a prism with a square base, sides of
8 inches, and a height of 12 inches.

CL 9-96.   Jamie bought a music player on sale for $65. The original price was $80. What
percent discount did she receive?

CL 9-97.   Manuela found a great deal on pens at 3 for $0.99. It was such a good deal that
she decided to buy two-dozen pens. How much did she pay for all of the pens?

CL 9-98. Shawn's science class has a ratio of 4:5, girls to boys.

    a.   What is the ratio of boys to girls?

    b.   What is the ratio of boys to total students?

    c.   What percent of the class is boys?

    d.   What fraction of the class is girls?

CL 9-99. Casey was building a rectangular pen for his pigs. He has 62 feet of fencing.
The length of his pen is 9 feet longer than the width. Write and solve an
equation to find the dimensions of the pen.

CL 9-100. Solve the following equations.

    a. $12 = \frac{6}{7}x$ b. $3x + (-4) = 2x + 9$ c. $3x - 8 = 4x + (-2)$

    d. $2(x - 3) = 1 - 3x$ e. $\frac{38}{6} = \frac{x}{18}$ f. $\frac{9}{x} = \frac{85}{10}$

CL 9-101. For each of the problems above, do the following:
- Draw a bar or number line that represents 0 to 10.

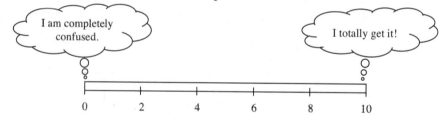

- Color or shade in a portion of the bar that represents your level of
understanding and comfort with completing that problem on your own.

If any of your bars are less than a 5, choose *one* of those problems and do one
of the following tasks:
- Write two questions that you would like to ask about that problem.
- Brainstorm two things that you DO know about that type of problem.

If all of your bars are a 5 or above, choose one of those problems and do one of
these tasks:
- Write two questions you might ask or hints you might give to a student
who was stuck on the problem.
- Make a new problem that is similar and more challenging than that
problem and solve it.

② WHAT TOOLS CAN I USE?

You have several tools and references available to help support your learning: your teacher, your study team, your math book, and your Toolkit, to name only a few. At the end of each chapter, you will have an opportunity to review your Toolkit for completeness. You will also revise or update it to reflect your current understanding of big ideas.

The main elements of your Toolkit should be your Learning Logs, Math Notes, and the vocabulary used in this chapter. Math words that are new appear in bold in the text. Refer to the lists provided below and follow your teacher's instructions to revise your Toolkit, which will help make it useful for you as you complete this chapter and as you work in future chapters.

Learning Log Entries
- Lesson 9.1.1 – Circumference and Diameter
- Lesson 9.1.2 – Area of Circles
- Lesson 9.2.1 – Surface Area of a Prism
- Lesson 9.2.4 – Volume of a Prism

Math Notes
- Lesson 9.1.2 – Circumference and Area of Circles
- Lesson 9.2.1 – Polygons, Prisms, and Pyramids
- Lesson 9.2.3 – Measurement in Different Dimensions
- Lesson 9.2.4 – Volume of a Prism

Mathematical Vocabulary
The following is a list of vocabulary found in this chapter. Some of the words have been seen in the previous chapter. The words in bold are words that are new to this chapter. Make sure that you are familiar with the terms below and know what they mean. For the words you do not know, refer to the glossary or index. You might also add these words to your Toolkit so that you can reference them in the future.

area	base	**circumference**
cross section	degree	**diameter**
edge	**face**	inference
irrational number	**lateral faces**	measurement
polygon	**polyhedron**	**pi (π)**
pyramid	**right rectangular prism**	**surface area**
vertex	**volume**	

Answers and Support for Closure Problems
What Have I Learned?

Note: MN = Math Note, LL = Learning Log

Problem	Solution	Need Help?	More Practice
CL 9-93.	$A \approx 132.7$ cm^2 $C \approx 40.8$ cm	Lessons 9.1.1 and 9.1.2 MN: 9.1.2 LL: 9.1.1, 9.1.2	Problems 9-10, 9-16, 9-31, 9-32, 9-47, 9-59, 9-78, and 9-90
CL 9-94.	a. SA = 1512 ft^2 V = 2744 ft^3 b. SA = 572 cm^2 V = 672 cm^3	Section 9.2 MN: 9.2.1, 9.2.3, and 9.2.4 LL: 9.2.1 and 9.2.4	Problems 9-56, 9-77, and 9-88
CL 9-95.	Surface area = 512 in.^{2} Volume = 768 in.^{3}	Section 9.2 MN: 9.2.1, 9.2.3, and 9.2.4 LL: 9.2.1 and 9.2.4	Problems 9-56, 9-77, and 9-88
CL 9-96.	About 19%	Lesson 7.1.7 MN: 7.1.7	Problems CL 7-120, CL 8-114, 9-18, 9-35, and 9-48
CL 9-97.	$7.92	Lessons 7.2.1 and 7.2.2 MN: 7.2.2 LL: 7.2.2	Problems CL 7-118, 9-14, 9-36, 9-50, 9-58, 9-67, 9-79, and 9-92
CL 9-98.	a. 5:4 b. 5:9 c. About 56% d. $\frac{4}{9}$	Lessons 5.1.1 and 5.1.2 MN: 5.1.1 and 5.1.2	Problems 5-18, 5-62, and 9-79

Problem	Solution	Need Help?	More Practice
CL 9-99.	$2x + 2(x+9) = 62$ OR $4x + 18 = 62$ The dimensions of the pen are 11 feet by 20 feet.	Section 5.3 and Lesson 6.2.4 MN: 5.3.3 and 6.2.4 LL: 5.3.4	Problems CL 6-144, CL 7-124, CL 8-116, and 9-81
CL 9-100.	a. $x = 14$ b. $x = 13$ c. $x = -6$ d. $x = \frac{7}{5} = 1.4$ e. $x = 114$ f. $x = \frac{90}{85} \approx 1.06$	Lessons 7.1.4, 7.1.5, and 7.1.6 MN: 7.1.6 LL: 7.1.5	Problems CL 7-121 and 9-92

9.3.1 How much should it cost?

Volume and Scaling

Have you ever made choices about which size of an item (such as a pizza or bottle of juice) to buy? If so, you may have considered which size was priced to give you the most for your money. In this lesson, you will work with your team as you analyze pricing of popcorn at a popular movie theater.

9-102.   The Maverick Movie Theater sells a small tub of popcorn for $1.

a. To keep its prices proportional to the amount of popcorn offered, what should the theater charge for the large tub shown at right? Show how you found your answer.

b. The medium-sized tub is a prism with a square base of 9 inches and a height of 12 inches. It currently costs $6 and is not selling well. The owner wants you to decide if this price is fair, as compared to the prices of the other sizes of popcorn tubs. How much should the medium tub cost if the owner wants it priced the same per cubic inch as the small tub? Write a note to the owner that explains whether the medium-sized tub is priced proportionally.

c. Customers have complained that the large tub is too wide to carry into the theater without spilling. The owner wants to change the base to be a 10-inch square instead. To keep the same volume, the owner thinks that the new tub will need to be 14 inches tall. She reasons that if the width gets two inches shorter, the height should grow by two inches.

Do you agree? If so, show how you know. If not, determine the new height of the tub.

d. The owner decided to create a new size that is 50% wider and 50% taller than the small tub. The owner plans to charge 50% more. Is this a good decision? If not, what should the owner charge and what percent increase is this price? Justify your answer.

Problem continues on next page. →

9-102.   *Problem continued from previous page.*

    e.   The owner wants to offer a tub of popcorn that would cost $6. She wants you to design the tub. Assume that the price should be proportional with the amount of popcorn in the small tub of popcorn. While the box can have any length, width, and height, be sure to make it a reasonable design for someone to hold and for the employees to fill with popcorn.

        Draw a diagram of your box with all measurements labeled.

9-103.   **MAKING CONNECTIONS**

When you solved the previous problem, you needed to use your knowledge about several different mathematical ideas.

    a.   With your team, do the following:

- Use colors to mark parts of your solution that used particular mathematical ideas. (For example, did you measure lengths? Did you draw quadrilaterals?)

- Label each mathematical idea with words in the margin of your paper.

    b.   Contribute your ideas to a class discussion. Did any other teams identify mathematical ideas that you used but had not noticed? If so, add these to your notes. Then write each mathematical idea on an index card.

    c.   How are these different mathematical ideas connected in this problem? Work with your team and follow your teacher's instructions to make a concept map. You will need to find ways to show or explain each of the connections you find.

9-104.   **BECOMING MATHEMATICALLY PROFICIENT**

During this course, you have been asked lots of different kinds of questions. The purpose of many of the questions is to help you think in new ways.

This book focuses on helping you use some very specific Mathematical Practices. The Mathematical Practices are different ways to approach a mathematics problem, pull it apart, and work on it. They include ways you communicate mathematics to your teammates and teacher. They are what make you a mathematician, not just a number cruncher!

Problem continues on next page. →

9-104. *Problem continued from previous page.*

Two of the Mathematical Practices you may have used in this lesson, for example, are **make sense of problems and persevere in solving them** and **construct viable arguments and critique the reasoning of others**. Below, you will learn more about what these mean.

a. With your team, read and discuss the descriptions below.

Make sense of problems and persevere in solving them:

Making sense of problems and persevering in solving them means that you can solve realistic problems that are full of different kinds of mathematics. These types of problems are not routine, simple, or typical. Instead, they combine lots of math ideas and real-life situations.

In this course, you made sense of such problems and persevered in solving them on a daily basis. You carried out investigations that were not simply "word problems." By making sense of a problem, rather than being told how to solve it step-by-step, you developed a deeper understanding of mathematics. You also learned how to carry out mathematical procedures fluently and efficiently.

In addition to learning and using problem-solving strategies, you had to stick with challenging problems, trying different strategies and using all of the resources available to you.

Construct viable arguments and critique the reasoning of others:

An important practice of mathematics is to **construct viable arguments and critique the reasoning of others**. In this course, you regularly shared information, opinions, and expertise with your study team. You took turns talking, listening, contributing, arguing, asking for help, checking for understanding, and keeping each other focused.

During this process, you learned to use higher-order thinking. "Critical thinking" is another way to describe "higher-order thinking." It can be difficult to learn, but it is extremely valuable. Learning how to think critically helped you understand concepts more deeply. It allowed you to apply newfound ideas in all sorts of problems, not just the specific concept you happened to be working on.

Problem continues on next page. →

9-104.   *Problem continued from previous page.*

You and your study teams used higher-order, critical-thinking skills any time you provided clarification, built on each other's ideas, analyzed a problem by breaking it into smaller parts, came to agreement during a discussion, and productively criticized each other's ideas.

Justifying and critiquing was a part of your daily classwork, not an occasional assignment. For each problem, you were expected to communicate your mathematical findings in writing, in oral presentations, or in poster presentations in a clear and convincing manner.

b.   How did you **make sense of problems and persevere in solving them** when you solved problem 9-102? Be ready to explain your ideas.

c.   How did you **construct viable arguments and critique the reasoning of others** while doing problem 9-102? How is **critiquing the reasoning of others** important in problems such as this one?

d.   Work with your team to brainstorm other problems in this course in which you **made sense of problems and persevered in solving them** and **constructed viable arguments and critiqued the reasoning of others**. Be ready to share your ideas with the class.

9.3.2 What is the best design?

Using Multiple Math Ideas to Create an Interior Design

Have you ever helped to decide how furniture should be arranged in a room? Or have you seen something that you liked and wondered if it would fit in your space? In this lesson, you will use several math ideas you have learned in this course to help figure out how to place furniture in a particular room. Then you will discuss what you have learned in this course that helps you solve complex problems like this one.

9-105.   DELIGHTFUL DESIGN

Laura is moving into a new bedroom. She is trying to decide how to arrange her furniture in her new room, but the only information she has about the size of her room is from the scale drawing shown at right.

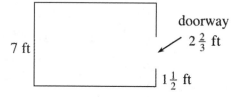

She has four pieces of bedroom furniture, with the dimensions given below.

Bed: 40 in. × 74 in.   Nightstand: 24 in. × 18 in.

Dresser: 26 in. × 18 in.   Desk: 52 in. × 22 in.

a. To plan the arrangement of the furniture, Laura needs to know the dimensions of the room. Find the missing wall measurements of Laura's bedroom.

b. Laura wants to draw a floor plan to make it easier to imagine how the furniture will fit into the space. Work with your team to decide on a scale factor, and draw a floor plan of Laura's bedroom on graph paper.

c. Laura wants to make paper cut-outs to represent her furniture so that she can arrange them on her floor plan. Each member of your team should choose one piece of furniture and draw a reduced version. (Be sure to reduce by the same amount as you did for your floor plan.) Then cut out the reduced pieces of furniture and move them around the floor plan to create an arrangement that Laura could use for her room.

d. How much walking space will Laura have in her bedroom? In other words, what is the area that is not covered with furniture?

9-106.   MAKING CONNECTIONS

When you solved this problem, you needed to use your learning about several different math ideas.

a.   Discuss this with your team.

   • Use colors to mark parts of your solution that used particular math ideas. (For example, did you add portions? Did you calculate measures of central tendency, such as mean or median?)

   • Label each math idea with words in the margin of your paper.

b.   Contribute your ideas to a class discussion. Did any other teams identify math ideas that you used but had not noticed? If so, add these to your notes. Then write each math idea on an index card.

c.   How are these different math ideas connected in this problem? Work with your team and follow your teacher's instructions to make a concept map. Work with your team to find ways to show or explain each of the connections you think of.

9-107.   BECOMING MATHEMATICALLY PROFICIENT

During this course, you have been asked lots of different kinds of questions. The purpose of many of the questions is to help you think in new ways.

This book focuses on helping you use some very specific Mathematical Practices. The Mathematical Practices are different ways to approach a mathematics problem, pull it apart, and work on it. They include ways you communicate mathematics to your teammates and teacher. They are what make you a mathematician, not just a number cruncher!

Two of the Mathematical Practices you may have used in this lesson, for example, are **look for and make use of structure** and **look for and express regularity in repeated reasoning**. Below, you will learn more about what these mean.

Problem continues on next page. →

9-107.   *Problem continued from previous page.*

a.   With your team, read and discuss the descriptions below.

Look for and make use of structure:

Looking for and making use of structure has been an important part of this course. Since you are working to develop a deep, conceptual understanding of mathematics, you often use this practice to bring closure to an investigation. There are many concepts that you have learned by looking at the underlying structure of a math idea and thinking about how it connects to other ideas you have already learned.

One example of when you looked at the underlying structure of a math idea is when you learned to simplify with the "Giant One." The "Giant One" was a structure to use in arithmetic with fractions, where the numerator and denominator are the same, giving you a value of 1.

By being involved in the actual development of math concepts, you gain a deeper understanding of mathematics than you would if you were simply told what they are and how to do related problems.

Look for and express regularity in repeated reasoning:

Look for and express regularity in repeated reasoning means that when you are faced with an investigation of a new mathematical concept, you sometimes look for a simpler or related problem. This strategy can help expand your ability to solve increasingly complex problems.

For example, you **looked for and expressed regularity in repeated reasoning** when you expanded the reasoning from simple probability situations to more complicated ones such as compound independent and dependent situations.

b.   How did **looking for and making use of structure** help you solve problem 9-105? Be ready to explain your ideas.

c.   Sometimes you **look for and express regularity in repeated reasoning** to help explain mathematics and to explain your thinking. How did **looking for regularity in repeated reasoning** help you make your scale drawing in problem 9-105?

d.   Work with your team to brainstorm other problems in this course in which you **looked for and expressed regularity in repeated reasoning** and **looked for and made use of structure**. Be ready to share your ideas with the class.

9.3.3 How can I use ratios?

Applying Ratios

Fish biologists need to keep track of fish populations in the waters they monitor. They want to know, for example, how many striped bass there are in San Francisco Bay. This number changes throughout the year as fish move in and out of the bay to spawn. Therefore, biologists need a way to gather current data quickly and inexpensively.

Today you and your team will model how scientists might make an estimate of the number of fish in a body of water using an application of ratios.

9-108.   **ESTIMATING FISH POPULATIONS**
         TEAM CHALLENGE

Your team will be given a "lake" (paper bag) with "fish" (beans). Do you think that you can find out how many fish are in your lake?

Your Task: Determine the number of fish in your lake as accurately as possible *without* actually counting the fish. Then count the fish to determine the accuracy of your method.

Discussion Points

What are you supposed to find? Explain this in your own words.

How do you think fish biologists determine the population of fish in a lake?

What information can you gather to help you answer this question?

What tools will you need?

Can you use ratios to determine the number of fish in your lake?
Why or why not?

9-109.   Since it is impossible to count every animal, biologists use a process called "tag and recapture" to help them estimate the size of a population. Tag and recapture involves collecting a sample of animals, tagging them, and releasing them back into the wild. Later, biologists collect a new sample of the animals and count the number first-time captures and recaptures in the sample. Then they use the data to estimate the population size.

Your team's task is to use the tag-and-recapture process to estimate the number of "fish" (beans) in your "lake" (paper bag).

a.   How many fish do you think are in your lake? Make an estimate.

b.   Use the "net" (small cup) to collect an initial sample. Carefully count the number of fish in the sample and record the data.

c.   To tag the fish, either replace each fish in the sample with a fish of a different color or mark both sides of each captured fish with a pen. Add these tagged fish to the lake. Be careful not to let any of the fish jump out onto the floor! If you replaced the fish with fish of different colors, then put the original fish from your sample aside. Do not return them to the lake, or else this will increase the number of fish in the lake.

d.   Gently shake the bag to mix the fish thoroughly. Then collect another sample. Count the number of tagged and untagged fish in this new sample. Record the information on your paper. Then return the entire sample to the lake.

e.   Look over the data you have collected so far. How many tagged fish are in the lake? How many tagged fish were in the second sample? What was the total number of fish in the second sample? Use this data and equivalent ratios to determine the total number of fish in the lake.

f.   Repeat the process outlined in parts (d) and (e) to get a second estimate of the total number of fish in the lake. Is this second estimate close to the first?

g.   **Extension:** Your solutions represent two estimates for the fish population of your lake. While it is important to get an accurate count, each time you net a sample, it costs taxpayers $500 for your time and equipment. So far, your samples have cost a total of $1000. If you think your estimate is accurate at this point, record it on the class table with your cost. If you think you should try another sample for better accuracy, do the same steps as before. Draw as many samples as you need, but remember that each sample costs $500.

h.   Count the fish in your lake to find the actual population. Then record your team's data on the class table. Use the mean of your estimates to represent your overall estimate of fish in the lake.

i.   Was your estimate close? Was it better than your estimate from part (a)? If not, what might have affected it? Do you think that this method of counting populations is accurate? Why or why not?

Core Connections, Course 2

9-110.   MAKING CONNECTIONS

When you solved this problem, you needed to use your knowledge about several different mathematical ideas.

a.   With your team do the following:

- Use colors to mark parts of your solution that used particular mathematical ideas. (For example, did you measure lengths? Did you draw quadrilaterals?)

- Label each mathematical idea with words in the margin of your paper.

b.   Contribute your ideas to a class discussion. Did any other teams identify mathematical ideas that you used but had not noticed? If so, add these to your notes. Then write each mathematical idea on an index card.

c.   How are these different mathematical ideas connected in this problem? Work with your team and follow your teacher's instructions to make a concept map. You will need to find ways to show or explain each of the connections you find.

9-111.   BECOMING MATHEMATICALLY PROFICIENT

During this course, you have been asked lots of different kinds of questions. The purpose of many of the questions is to help you think in new ways.

This book focuses on helping you use some very specific Mathematical Practices. The Mathematical Practices are different ways to approach a mathematics problem, pull it apart, and work on it. They include ways you communicate mathematics to your teammates and teacher. They are what make you a mathematician, not just a number cruncher!

Two of the Mathematical Practices you may have used in this lesson, for example, are **model with mathematics** and **use appropriate tools**. Below, you will learn more about what these mean.

a.   With your team, read and discuss the descriptions below.

Model with mathematics:

When you **model with mathematics**, you are not wearing fancy clothes on a runway in New York! Mathematical modeling is what you do when you work with situations that involve multiple representations. For example, in this course, you frequently modeled different relationships and patterns using tables, graphs, equations, and words or diagrams.

Problem continues on next page. →

9-111.   *Problem continued from previous page.*

In creating these models, you often first make assumptions, then make predictions, and finally check to see if your predictions make sense in the context of the problem.

In situations involving the variability of data, you learned that although a model may not be perfect, it can still be very useful for describing data and making predictions. You also found that a calculator or computer can help you model situations more efficiently than doing the work by hand.

Use appropriate tools strategically:

Throughout this course, you had to **use appropriate tools strategically**. In a typical lesson, you had many different tools available to you. Examples of tools include rulers, scissors, diagrams, graph paper, blocks, tiles, and calculators. However, you were not usually told which specific tools to use to solve any particular problem.

Sometimes, different teams decided to use different tools to solve the same problem. Thus, you often shared your solution strategies with the whole class. Frequently, this included a discussion about which tools were most efficient and productive to solve a given problem.

As you continued to do more and more sophisticated mathematics throughout the course, you were introduced to other tools, such as computer applications.

b. How did you **model with mathematics** while doing problem 9-109? How is **modeling** important in problems such as this one?

c. How did you **use appropriate tools strategically** when you solved problem 9-109? Be ready to explain your ideas.

d. Work with your team to brainstorm other problems in this course in which you **modeled with mathematics** and **used appropriate tools strategically**. Be ready to share your ideas with the class.

Core Connections, Course 2
Checkpoint Materials

Notes to Students (and their Teachers)

Students master different skills at different speeds. No two students learn exactly the same way at the same time. At some point you will be expected to perform certain skills accurately. Most of the Checkpoint problems incorporate skills that you should have been developing in grades 5 and 6. If you have not mastered these skills yet it does not mean that you will not be successful in this class. However, you may need to do some work outside of class to get caught up on them.

Starting in Chapter 1 and finishing in Chapter 9, there are 9 problems designed as Checkpoint problems. Each one is marked with an icon like the one above and numbered according to the chapter that it is in. After you do each of the Checkpoint problems, check your answers by referring to this section. If your answers are incorrect, you may need some extra practice to develop that skill. The practice sets are keyed to each of the Checkpoint problems in the textbook. Each has the topic clearly labeled, followed by the answers to the corresponding Checkpoint problem and then some completed examples. Next, the complete solution to the Checkpoint problem from the text is given, and there are more problems for you to practice with answers included.

Remember, looking is not the same as doing! You will never become good at any sport by just watching it, and in the same way, reading through the worked examples and understanding the steps is not the same as being able to do the problems yourself. How many of the extra practice problems do you need to try? That is really up to you. Remember that your goal is to be able to do similar problems on your own confidently and accurately. This is your responsibility. You should not expect your teacher to spend time in class going over the solutions to the Checkpoint problem sets. If you are not confident after reading the examples and trying the problems, you should get help outside of class time or talk to your teacher about working with a tutor.

Checkpoint Topics

1.   Area and Perimeter of Polygons
2.   Multiple Representations of Portions
3.   Multiplying Fractions and Decimals
5   Order of Operations
6.   Writing and Evaluating Algebraic Expressions
7A. Simplifying Expressions
7B. Displays of Data: Histograms and Box Plots
8.   Solving Multi-Step Equations
9.   Unit Rates and Proportions

Checkpoint 6

Problem 6-139

Writing and Evaluating Algebraic Expressions

Answers to problem 6-139: a. $x+6$, b. $y-5$, c. $2x+3$, d. $5y$, e. 11; 3; 13; 40

There are some vocabulary words that are frequently used to represent arithmetic operations.

Addition is often suggested by: sum, increased, more than, greater than, total

Subtraction is often suggested by: difference, decreased by, less than, smaller than

Multiplication is often suggested by: product, times, twice, double

Division is often suggested by: quotient, divided by, shared evenly

Examples

Five more than m:
Five more than a number, increases a number by 5 so it would be $m+5$.

Three less than x:
Three less than a number makes the number smaller by 3 so it would be $x-3$.

Triple m:
Tripling a number is the same as multiplying the number by 3 so it would be $3m$.

Five divided by x:
Division is usually written as a fraction so it would be $\frac{5}{x}$.

To evaluate an algebraic expression means to calculate the value of the expression when the variable is replaced by a numerical value.

Examples

Evaluate $2x-5$ if $x=7$ Solution: $2x-5 \Rightarrow 2\cdot 7-5 = 14-5 = 9$

Evaluate $\frac{6}{x}+9$ if $x=2$ Solution: $\frac{6}{x}+9 \Rightarrow \frac{6}{2}+9 = 3+9 = 12$

Now we can go back and solve the original problem. Part (e) is included with the writing of the expression.

a. Six more suggests adding 6 so it would be $x+6$; if $x=5$ then $x+6 \Rightarrow 5+6 = 11$.

b. Five less suggests subtracting 5 so it would be $y-5$; if $y=8$ then $y-5 \Rightarrow 8-5 = 3$.

c. Twice a number suggests multiplication by 2 and then increasing by 3 means to add 3 to the previous product so it would be $2x+3$; if $x=5$ then $2x+3 \Rightarrow 2\cdot 5+3 = 13$.

d. Product suggests multiply so it would be $5y$; if $y=8$ then $5y \Rightarrow 5\cdot 8 = 40$.

Here are some more to try. For problems 1 through 16 write an algebraic expression. For problems 17 through 24 evaluate the expression for the given values.

1. 5 greater than m
2. Double s
3. 7 less than t
4. 6 more than y
5. 14 divided by b
6. m subtracted from a
7. x divided among 5
8. The product of 7 and e
9. The sum of d and l
10. 6 times c
11. The product of x, y, and w
12. h times 8, added to j
13. 4 divided by p, increased by 7
14. Half of r
15. Three times q increased by 5
16. Two less than triple n
17. $4x - 3$ if $x = 5$
18. $7d$ if $d = 10$
19. $2xy + 1$ if $x = 3$, $y = 4$
20. $4 + 8g$ if $g = 6$
21. $4b + 12$ if $b = 11$
22. $\frac{9g}{27}$ if $g = 3$
23. $mw + h$ if $m = 5, w = 8, h = 6$
24. $\frac{y}{z} + 7$ if $y = 4, z = 2$

Answers:

1. $m + 5$
2. $2s$
3. $t - 7$
4. $y + 6$
5. $\frac{14}{b}$
6. $a - m$
7. $\frac{x}{5}$
8. $7e$
9. $d + l$
10. $6c$
11. xyw
12. $8h + j$
13. $\frac{4}{p} + 7$
14. $\frac{r}{2}$
15. $3q + 5$
16. $3n - 2$
17. 17
18. 70
19. 25
20. 52
21. 56
22. 1
23. 46
24. 9

Checkpoint 7A

Problem 7-50

Simplifying Expressions

Answers to problem 7-50: a. $2x^2 + x - 10$, b. $x^2 - 9x + 11$

Like terms are two or more terms that are exactly the same except for their coefficients. That is, they have the same variable(s), with corresponding variable(s) raised to the same power. Like terms can be combined into one quantity by adding and/or subtracting the coefficients of the terms. Terms are usually listed in the order of decreasing powers of the variable. Combining like terms, one way of simplifying expressions, using algebra tiles is shown in the first two examples.

Example 1:

Simplify $(2x^2 + 4x + 5) + (x^2 + x + 3)$ means combine $2x^2 + 4x + 5$ with $x^2 + x + 3$.

$$(2x^2 + 4x + 5) + (x^2 + x + 3) = 3x^2 + 5x + 8$$

Example 2:

Simplify $x^2 + 3x - 4 + 2(2x^2 - x) + 3$.

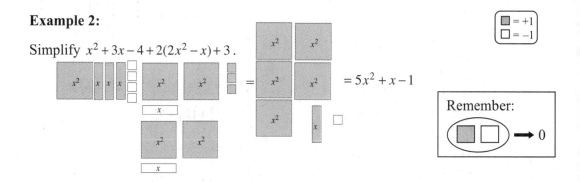

$$= 5x^2 + x - 1$$

$\square = +1$
$\square = -1$

Remember:

$\left(\square\square\right) \longrightarrow 0$

Now we can go back and solve the original problem.

a. $\quad 4x^2 + 3x - 7 + -2x^2 - 2x + (-3)$

$\quad (4x^2 - 2x^2) + (3x - 2x) + (-7 + (-3))$

$\quad\quad\quad 2x^2 + x - 10$

b. $\quad -3x^2 - 2x + 5 + 4x^2 - 7x + 6$

$\quad (-3x^2 + 4x^2) + (-2x - 7x) + (5 + 6)$

$\quad\quad\quad x^2 - 9x + 11$

Here are some more to try.

1. $(x^2 + 3x + 4) + (x^2 + 3x + 2)$

2. $x^2 + 4x + 3 + x^2 + 2x + 5$

3. $2x^2 + 2x - 1 + x^2 - 4x + 5$

4. $3x^2 - x + 7 - 3x^2 + 2x + (-4)$

5. $2x^2 + 4x + (-3) + x^2 - 3x + 5$

6. $4x^2 + 2x - 8 + (-2x^2) + 5x + 1$

7. $-4x^2 + 2x + 8 - 3x^2 + 5x - 3$

8. $3x^2 + 2(4x + 1) - 2x^2 + 4x + 5$

9. $3(5x^2 + 4x) - 7 + 2x + 3$

10. $3x^2 - 4x + 2 + 4(2x^2 + 2x)$

11. $-2(3x^2 - x + 2) + 3x - 1$

12. $2(x^2 - 2x) + 7 + 5(x^2 + 4x) - 3$

13. $2x^2 - 3(x - 3) + 5x^2 - 4x$

14. $-3x + 3(x^2 + 2) + (-x) - 4$

15. $(x^2 + 3x + 2) - (x^2 - 3x - 2)$

16. $(2x^2 - 5x) - (x^2 + 7x)$

17. $(5x + 6) - (x^2 - 5x + 6)$

18. $4a + 2b + 3c - 6a + 3b - 6c$

19. $3c + 4a - 7c + 5b - (-4a) + 7$

20. $-5a + 6b - 7c - (3c - 4b - a)$

Answers:

1. $2x^2 + 6x + 6$

2. $2x^2 + 6x + 8$

3. $3x^2 - 2x + 4$

4. $x + 3$

5. $3x^2 + x + 2$

6. $2x^2 + 7x - 7$

7. $-7x^2 + 7x + 5$

8. $x^2 + 12x + 7$

9. $15x^2 + 14x - 4$

10. $11x^2 + 4x + 2$

11. $-6x^2 + 5x - 5$

12. $7x^2 + 16x + 4$

13. $7x^2 - 7x + 9$

14. $3x^2 - 4x + 2$

15. $6x + 4$

16. $x^2 - 12x$

17. $-x^2 + 10x$

18. $-2a + 5b - 3c$

19. $8a + 5b - 7c + 7$

20. $-4a + 10b - 10c$

Checkpoint 7B

Problem 7-117

Displays of Data: Histograms and Box Plots

Answers to problem 7-117:

a.   b.   c.

d.

c: IQR = 4   d: IQR = 14

Histograms

A histogram is a method of showing data. It uses a bar to show the frequency (the number of times something occurs). The frequency measures something that changes numerically. (In a bar graph the frequency measures something that changes by category.) The intervals (called bins) for the data are shown on the horizontal axis and the frequency is represented by the height of a rectangle above the interval. The labels on the horizontal axis represent the lower end of each interval or bin.

Example: Sam and her friends weighed themselves and here is their weight in pounds: 110, 120, 131, 112, 125, 135, 118, 127, 135, and 125. Make a histogram to display the information. Use intervals of 10 pounds.

Solution:

See histogram at right. Note that the person weighing 120 pounds is counted in the next higher bin.

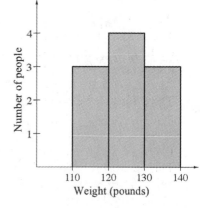

Box Plots

A box plot displays a summary of data using the median, quartiles, and extremes of the data. The box contains the "middle half" of the data. The right segment represents the top 25% of the data and the left segment represent the bottom 25% of the data.

Example: Create a box plot for the set of data given in the previous example.

Solution: Place the data in order to find the median (middle number) and the quartiles (middle numbers of the upper half and the lower half.)

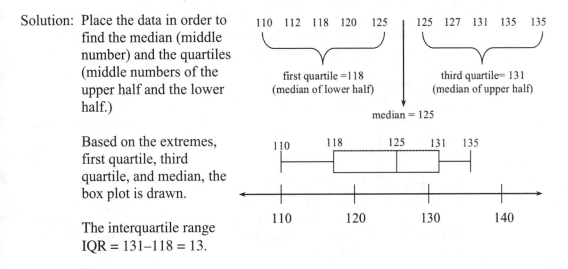

Based on the extremes, first quartile, third quartile, and median, the box plot is drawn.

The interquartile range IQR = 131–118 = 13.

Now we can go back to the original problem.

a. The 0–1 bin contains the six students who do less than one hour of homework. The 1–2 bin contains the 10 students who do at least one hour but less than two hours. The 2–3 bin contains the seven students who do at least two hours but less than three hours. There are no students who do at least three hours and less than four. Two students did four hours and less than five. See the histogram above.

b. The 0–5 bin contains two scores less than 5 points. The 5–10 bin contains the two scores of a least five but less than 10. The 10–15 bin contains the eight scores at least 10 but less than 15. The 15–20 bin contains the seven scores at least 15 but less than 20. See the histogram above.

c. Place the ages in order: 46, 46, 47, 47, 48, 49, 50, 51, 52.
The median is the middle age: 48. The first quartile is the median of the lower half of the ages. Since there are four lower-half ages, the median is the average of the middle two: $\frac{46+47}{2} = 46.5$. The third quartile is the median of the upper half ages. Again, there are four upper-half ages, so average the two middle ages: $\frac{50+51}{2} = 50.5$. The interquartile range is the difference between the third quartile and the first quartile: 50.5–46.5 = 4. See the box plot above.

d. Place the scores in order: 70, 72, 75, 76, 80, 82, 85, 90, 93.
The median is the middle score: 80. The lower quartile is the median of the lower half of the scores. Since there are four lower-half scores, the median is the average of the middle two: $\frac{72+75}{2} = 73.5$. The third quartile is the median of the upper half of the scores. Again, there are four upper-half scores, so average the two middle ages: $\frac{85+90}{2} = 87.5$. The interquartile range is the difference between the third quartile and the first quartile: 87.5–73.5 = 14. See the box plot above.

Here are some more to try. For problems 1 through 6, create a histogram. For problems 7 through 12, create a box plot. State the quartiles and the interquartile range.

1. Number of heads showing in 20 tosses of three coins:
   2, 2, 1, 3, 1, 0, 2, 1, 2, 1, 1, 2, 0, 1, 3, 2, 1, 3, 1, 2

2. Number of even numbers in 5 rolls of a dice done 14 times:
   4, 2, 2, 3, 1, 2, 1, 1, 3, 3, 2, 2, 4, 5

3. Number of fish caught by 7 fishermen:
   2, 3, 0, 3, 3, 1, 5

4. Number of girls in grades K-8 at local schools:
   12, 13, 15, 10, 11, 12, 15, 11, 12

5. Number of birthdays in each March in various 2nd grade classes:
   5, 1, 0, 0, 2, 4, 4, 1, 3, 1, 0, 4

6. Laps jogged by 15 students:
   10, 15, 10, 13, 20, 14, 17, 10, 15, 20, 8, 7, 13, 15, 12

7. Number of days of rain:
   6, 8, 10, 9, 7, 7, 11, 12, 6, 12, 14, 10

8. Number of times a frog croaked per minute:
   38, 23, 40, 12, 35, 27, 51, 26, 24, 14, 38, 41, 23, 17

9. Speed in mph of 15 different cars:
   30, 35, 40, 23, 33, 32, 28, 37, 30, 31, 29, 33, 39, 22, 30

10. Typing speed of 12 students in words per minute:
    28, 30, 60, 26, 47, 53, 39, 42, 48, 27, 23, 86

11. Number of face cards pulled when 13 cards are drawn 15 times:
    1, 4, 2, 1, 1, 0, 0, 2, 1, 3, 3, 0, 0, 2, 1

12. Height of 15 students in inches:
    48, 55, 56, 65, 67, 60, 60, 57, 50, 59, 62, 65, 58, 70, 68

Answers:

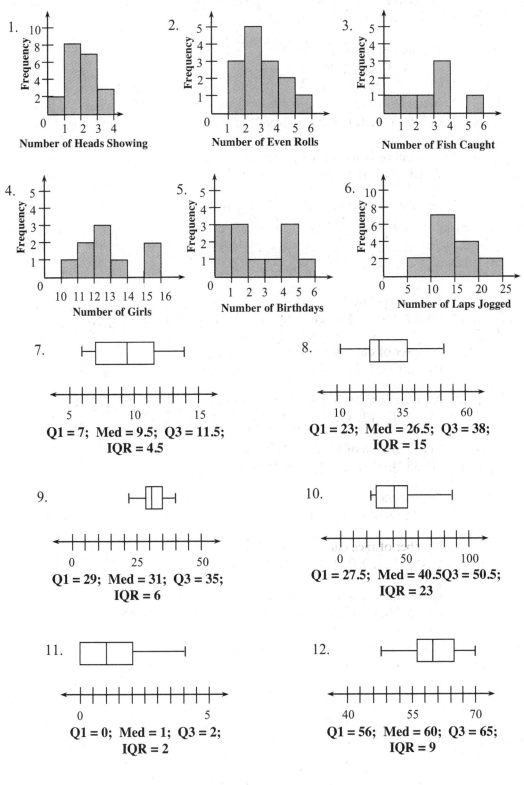

1. Number of Heads Showing

2. Number of Even Rolls

3. Number of Fish Caught

4. Number of Girls

5. Number of Birthdays

6. Number of Laps Jogged

7. Q1 = 7; Med = 9.5; Q3 = 11.5; IQR = 4.5

8. Q1 = 23; Med = 26.5; Q3 = 38; IQR = 15

9. Q1 = 29; Med = 31; Q3 = 35; IQR = 6

10. Q1 = 27.5; Med = 40.5 Q3 = 50.5; IQR = 23

11. Q1 = 0; Med = 1; Q3 = 2; IQR = 2

12. Q1 = 56; Med = 60; Q3 = 65; IQR = 9

Checkpoint 8

Problem 8-109

Solving Multi-Step Equations

Answers to problem 8-109: a: $x = 7$, b: $x = -2$, c: $x = 0$, d: $x = \frac{2}{3}$

A general strategy for solving equations is to first simplify each side of the equation. Next isolate the variable on one side and the constants on the other by adding equal values on both sides of the equation or removing balanced sets or zeros. Finally determine the value of the variable–usually by division.

Note: When the process of solving an equation ends with different numbers on each side of the equal sign (for example, $2 = 4$), there is *no solution* to the problem. When the result is the same expression or number on each side of the equation (for example, $x + 2 = x + 2$) it means that *all numbers* are solutions.

Example 1: Solve $3x + 3x - 1 = 4x + 9$

Solution

$3x + 3x - 1 = 4x + 9$	problem
$6x - 1 = 4x + 9$	simplify by combining like terms
$2x = 10$	add 1, subtract $4x$ on each side
$x = 5$	divide by 2

Example 2: Solve $-2x + 1 + 3(x - 1) = -4 + -x - 2$

Solution

$-2x + 1 + 3(x - 1) = -4 + -x - 2$	problem
$-2x + 1 + 3x - 3 = -x - 6$	distribute the 3 on the left side
$x - 2 = -x - 6$	simplify by combining like terms
$2x = -4$	add x, add 2 to each side
$x = -2$	divide by 2

Now we can go back and solve the original problem.

a. $24 = 3x + 3$
$21 = 3x$
$7 = x$

b. $6x + 12 = -x - 2$
$6x = -x - 14$
$7x = -14$
$x = -2$

c. $3x + 3 - x + 2 = x + 5$
$2x + 5 = x + 5$
$2x = x$
$x = 0$

d. $5(x - 1) = 5(4x - 3)$
$5x - 5 = 20x - 15$
$5x = 20x - 10$
$-15x = -10$
$x = \frac{-10}{-15} = \frac{2}{3}$

Here are some more to try.

1. $2x + 3 = -7$

2. $-3x - 2 = -1$

3. $3x + 2 + x = x + 5$

4. $4x - 2 - 2x = x - 5$

5. $2x - 3 = -x + 3$

6. $1 + 3x - x = x - 4 + 2x$

7. $4 - 3x = 2x - 6$

8. $3 + 3x - x + 2 = 3x + 4$

9. $-x - 3 = 2x - 6$

10. $-4 + 3x - 1 = 2x + 1 + 2x$

11. $-x + 3 = 6$

12. $5x - 3 + 2x = x + 2 + x$

13. $2x - 7 = -x - 1$

14. $-2 + 3x = x - 2 - 4x$

15. $-3x + 7 = x - 1$

16. $1 + 2x - 4 = -3 + x$

17. $3(x + 2) = x + 2$

18. $2(x - 2) + x = 5$

19. $10 = x + 5 + x$

20. $-x + 2 = x - 5 - 3x$

21. $3x + 2 - x = x - 2 + x$

22. $4x + 12 = 2x - 8$

23. $3(4 + x) = x + 6$

24. $6 - x - 3 = 4(x - 2)$

Answers:

1. $x = -5$

2. $x = -\frac{1}{3}$

3. $x = 1$

4. $x = -3$

5. $x = 2$

6. $x = 5$

7. $x = 2$

8. $x = 1$

9. $x = 1$

10. $x = -6$

11. $x = -3$

12. $x = 1$

13. $x = 2$

14. $x = 0$

15. $x = 2$

16. $x = 0$

17. $x = -2$

18. $x = 3$

19. $x = 2\frac{1}{2}$

20. $x = -7$

21. no solution

22. $x = -10$

23. $x = -3$

24. $x = 2\frac{1}{5}$

Checkpoint 9

Problem 9-92

Unit Rates and Proportions

Answers to problem 9-92: a: 24 mpg; b: $0.19; c: $x = 8$; d: $m = 32.5$

A rate is a ratio comparing two quantities and a unit rate has a denominator of one after simplifying. Unit rates or proportions may be used to solve ratio problems. Solutions may also be approximated by looking at graphs of lines passing through the origin and the given information.

Example 1: Judy's grape vine grew 15 inches in 6 weeks. What is the unit growth rate (inches per week)?

Solution: The growth rate is $\frac{15 \text{ inches}}{6 \text{ weeks}}$. To create a unit rate we need a denominator of "one." $\frac{15 \text{ inches}}{6 \text{ weeks}} = \frac{x \text{ inches}}{1 \text{ week}}$. Solve by using a Giant One: $\frac{15 \text{ inches}}{6 \text{ weeks}} = \boxed{\frac{6}{6}} \frac{x \text{ inches}}{1 \text{ week}} \Rightarrow 2.5 \frac{\text{inches}}{\text{week}}$

Example 2: Bob's favorite oatmeal raisin cookie recipe use 3 cups of raisins for 5 dozen cookies. How many cups are needed for 40 dozen cookies?

Solution: The rate is $\frac{3 \text{ cups}}{5 \text{ dozen}}$ so the problem may be written as this proportion: $\frac{3}{5} = \frac{c}{40}$.

One method of solving the proportion is to use a Giant One:

$$\tfrac{3}{5} = \tfrac{c}{40} \Rightarrow \tfrac{3}{5} \boxed{\tfrac{8}{8}} = \tfrac{24}{40} \Rightarrow c = 24$$

Another method is to think about unit rates. Since the unit rate is $\frac{3}{5}$ cup per dozen, one could also take the unit rate and multiply by the number of units needed: $\frac{3}{5} \cdot 40 = 24$.

Using either method the answer is 24 cups of raisins.

Now we can go back and solve the original problem.

a. $\frac{108 \text{ miles}}{4.5 \text{ gallons}} = \boxed{\frac{4.5}{4.5}} \cdot \frac{x \text{ miles}}{1 \text{ gallon}} \Rightarrow 24 \frac{\text{miles}}{\text{gallon}}$

b. $\frac{\$3.23}{17 \text{ oranges}} = \boxed{\frac{17}{17}} \frac{x}{1 \text{ orange}} \Rightarrow 0.19 \frac{\$}{\text{orange}}$

c. Using a Giant One:

$\frac{x}{12} \boxed{\frac{2.5}{2.5}} = \frac{2.5x}{30} = \frac{20}{30} \Rightarrow 20 = 2.5x \Rightarrow x = 8$

d. Using the Giant One

$\frac{13}{40} \boxed{\frac{2.5}{2.5}} = \frac{32.5}{100} \Rightarrow m = 32.5$

Here are some more to try. For problems 1 through 8 find the unit rate. For problems 17 through 24 solve the proportion.

1. Typing 544 words in 17 minutes (words per minute)

2. Taking 92 minutes to run 10 miles (minutes per mile)

3. Reading 258 pages in 86 minutes (pages per minute)

4. Falling 385 feet in 35 seconds (feet per second)

5. Buying 15 boxes of cereal for $39.75 ($ per box)

6. Drinking 28 bottles of water in 8 days (bottles per day)

7. Scoring 98 points in a 40 minute game (points per minute)

8. Planting 76 flowers in 4 hours (flowers per hour)

9. $\frac{3}{8} = \frac{x}{50}$

10. $\frac{2}{5} = \frac{x}{75}$

11. $\frac{7}{9} = \frac{14}{x}$

12. $\frac{24}{25} = \frac{96}{x}$

13. $\frac{15}{9} = \frac{12}{x}$

14. $\frac{45}{60} = \frac{x}{4}$

15. $\frac{4}{7} = \frac{18}{x}$

16. $\frac{8}{9} = \frac{72}{x}$

17. $\frac{3}{5} = \frac{x}{17}$

18. $\frac{17}{30} = \frac{51}{x}$

19. $\frac{5}{8} = \frac{16}{x}$

20. $\frac{3}{22} = \frac{15}{x}$

21. $\frac{1}{5} = \frac{x}{27}$

22. $\frac{x}{11} = \frac{8}{15}$

23. $\frac{14}{17} = \frac{x}{34}$

24. $\frac{12}{15} = \frac{36}{x}$

Answers:

1. $32 \frac{\text{words}}{\text{minute}}$

2. $9.2 \frac{\text{minutes}}{\text{mile}}$

3. $3 \frac{\text{pages}}{\text{minute}}$

4. $11 \frac{\text{feet}}{\text{second}}$

5. $2.65 \frac{\text{dollars}}{\text{box}}$

6. $3.5 \frac{\text{bottles}}{\text{day}}$

7. $2.45 \frac{\text{points}}{\text{minute}}$

8. $19 \frac{\text{flowers}}{\text{hour}}$

9. $x = 18.75$

10. $x = 30$

11. $x = 18$

12. $x = 100$

13. $x = 7.2$

14. $x = 3$

15. $x = 31.5$

16. $x = 81$

17. $x = 10.2$

18. $x = 90$

19. $x = 25.6$

20. $x = 110$

21. $x = 5.4$

22. $x = 5\frac{13}{15}$

23. $x = 28$

24. $x = 45$

Puzzle Investigator Problems

Dear Students,

Puzzle Investigator problems (PIs) present you with an opportunity to investigate complex, interesting problems. Their purpose is to focus on the process of solving complex problems. **You will be evaluated on your ability to show, explain, and justify your work and thoughts**. Save *all* of your work, including what does not work, in order to write about the processes you used to reach your answer.

Completion of a Puzzle Investigator problem includes four parts:

- **Problem Statement:** State the problem clearly in your own words so that anyone reading your paper will understand the problem you intend to solve.

- **Process and Solutions:** Describe in detail your thinking and reasoning as you work from start to finish. Explain your solution and how you know it is correct. Add diagrams when it helps your explanation. Include what you do that does not work and changes you make along the way. If you do not complete this problem, describe what you <u>do</u> know and where and why you are stuck.

- **Reflection:** Reflect about your learning and your reaction to the problem. What mathematics did you learn from it? What did you learn about your math problem solving strategies? Is this problem similar to any other problems you have done before? If yes, how?

- **Attached work:** Include <u>all</u> your work and notes. Your scratch work is important because it is a record of your thinking. Do not throw anything away.

PI-8.   PASCAL'S TRIANGLE

The number pattern started at right is called
Pascal's Triangle. While it looks like a
simple arrangement of numbers, it has many
interesting patterns within it. In this
challenge, you will learn more about the
hidden patterns of Pascal's Triangle.

a. Using the PI-8 Resource Page
    (which you can download at
    www.cpm.org), use the patterns to
    complete the missing numbers.
    Some of the numbers are given so
    you can check your work.

b. What is the sum of the 20th row of the triangle? Can you find this without
    extending the triangle? Explain how you found your answer.

c. Using a see-through highlighter, color in the squares that contain odd
    numbers. Describe the pattern that emerges.

d. Find at least three other patterns in Pascal's Triangle that you have not
    described so far.

PI-9. TILING THE LAUNDRY ROOM

Travis is planning to tile his laundry room with large L-shaped tiles made with 3 squares. (See an example at right.) According to his floor plan, the room is a 4 ft.× 4 ft. square. There is a drain in the floor that cannot be covered and is shaded in the diagram.

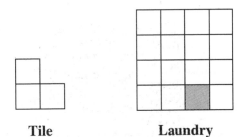

Tile

Laundry Room Floor

a. Show one way that Travis could tile his floor using his L-shaped tiles without breaking tiles and so that no tiles overlap or cover the drain. Use colors to help distinguish the tiles in your diagram. Is there more than one way to tile his floor?

b. While at the store, Travis suddenly worried that his diagram is wrong and he cannot remember where the drain is located. Does it matter? Can the floor be tiled no matter where the drain is located? Test the different possible locations of the drain (listed below) and write a short note to Travis about what you discovered.

    i.   Drain is located in the middle   *ii.*   Drain is located in the corner

c. Uh oh! Travis came home with his tiles and found out that his floor is actually a 5 ft.× 5 ft. square and the drain is in the corner. (This is why measurements should always be checked twice!) Luckily, he bought extra tiles. However, can this floor be tiled? Using graph paper, draw a diagram of Travis' laundry room floor and find a way he can tile his floor with the same L-shaped tiles.

d. Given that his laundry room is a 5 ft.× 5 ft. square, does it matter where the drain is located? Find at least one more location (not in the corner) for the drain that would allow Travis to tile the floor. Also find at least one location for the drain that would not allow the floor to be tiled without breaking a tile.

PI-10.   WAY TO GO!

The map at right shows the
streets in Old Town. Assume
Jacqueline is standing at the
corner of A and 1st Streets.
Assume Jacqueline will only
walk South or East. The
shaded rectangles represent
large buildings. Assume
Jacqueline will not pass
through any buildings.

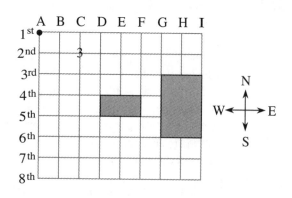

a.   The number "3" at the intersection of C and 2nd Streets means that there are
     three different ways she can get there from her starting position. What are
     those three ways? Describe them in words.

b.   How many different ways can she walk to the corner of F and 4th Streets?

c.   How many different ways can she walk to the corner of D and 5th Streets?

d.   Explain how you can use your answers to parts (b) and (c) to find the
     number of ways she can walk to the corner of F and 5th Streets. Why does
     this make sense?

e.   Find the number of different ways she can walk to the corner of I and 8th
     Streets.

f.   How could you change the map so that Jacqueline has only 7 ways to get to
     the corner of D and 3rd streets? You can remove blocks or add them.

PI-11.   WITH OR WITHOUT FROSTING

Mr. Hamada baked a cake for his class that was in the
shape of a big cube. As he carried the cake over to the
frosting table, he slipped and the cake fell into a large
tub of frosting!

Amazingly, the cake stayed in one piece, but all 6 sides
were now frosted. One student suggested the cake be
cut into cube-shaped pieces, all the same size.

a.   There are 32 students in Mr. Hamada's class and he does not want more
      than 100 pieces of cake. If Mr. Hamada cuts the cake into cube-shaped
      pieces, all the same size, how many pieces of cake should he cut so that
      everyone could have a piece? (Note: You might want to use small blocks
      to explore this question.)

b.   A student noticed that some pieces have
      no frosting, while others have 1, 2, or 3
      sides frosted. How many of each type of
      piece can Mr. Hamada offer?

c.   There were many students that wanted a
      piece with frosting on 3 sides, so Mr.
      Hamada changed his mind and decided to
      cut the cake into 125 cube-shaped pieces,
      all the same size. Did this increase the
      number of pieces with frosting on
      3 sides? Why or why not?

PI-12. CANDY SALES

For a fundraiser, each math club member must sell 30 candy bars each day for a week. Although they all sold the same type of candy, the members could choose their price to compete for top sales member.

Alfredo decided to sell three candy bars for $1, earning $10 per day, while June sold hers at the rate of two for $1, earning her $15 per day.

One day, both Alfredo and June were on a field trip, so they asked Bomani to sell their candy bars for them. Bomani agreed and promised he would not change their prices. Bomani decided that instead of offering three for $1 and two for $1, he would put them together and sell the 60 candy bars at the rate of five for $2.

When Alfredo and June returned, Bomani handed them the money he had earned for the day, $24. Alfredo and June were angry and demanded the dollar they were sure Bomani stole! Bomani is now confused... what happened?

Your Task: Discover what really happened to the extra dollar, and write a letter to Alfredo and June before this scene turns really ugly.

PI-13. TO TELL THE TRUTH

Alicia, Ben, Cassie, and Daryl shared some birthday cake before going into the living room to work on their homework. During the rest of the afternoon, each one of them left the room by themselves for a few minutes.

When they finished their homework, they went into the kitchen and discovered that the rest of the cake was missing. Below are their statements:

> Alicia: *"Ben ate it!"*
>
> Cassie: *"I didn't eat it!"*
>
> Ben: *"Daryl must have eaten it."*
>
> Daryl: *"Ben is lying."*

a. If only one of these statements is a lie, who ate the rest of the cake? Explain how you know which statement is false.

b. If only one of the above statements is the truth, who ate the rest of the cake? Explain how you know which statement is true.

c. While sorting out this mess, Ben's dad said, "What I am saying is not true." Is this statement true or false? Explain.

PI-14.   SECRET CODE

Arianna wants to send a secret code through her computer. By using a two-digit number for every letter, she can build secret words with numbers. For example, using her code below, "SECRET" becomes "180402170419."

A	B	C	D	E	F	G	H	I	J	K	L	M
00	01	02	03	04	05	06	07	08	09	10	11	12

N	O	P	Q	R	S	T	U	V	W	X	Y	Z
13	14	15	16	17	18	19	20	21	22	23	24	25

a.   To answer the question "who is your favorite mathematician," Arianna wrote 00170207081204030418. Decipher her message. Remember that every pair of numbers represents a letter.

b.   To send secret messages through computers, the numeric codes must be changed so that they only contain the digits 0 and 1. These are called **binary codes**, and use the base-2 number system. The base-2 number system counts in sets of 2 instead of sets of 10. The first 12 counting numbers in base-2 are shown in the table below. Based on this counting system, how would you write "12" in base-2? What about 15? 16?

Base 10:	00	01	02	03	04	05	06	07	08	09	10	11
Base 2:	00	01	10	11	100	101	110	111	1000	1001	1010	1011

c.   To make a computer code for the entire alphabet, plus a code for a space and a code for an exclamation point, you will need the base-2 equivalents for the numbers 0 through 27. The codes will have 5 digits so that every letter has the same number of digits. Copy and complete the table below.

A = 00	00000	H = 07		O = 14	01110	V = 21	
B = 01	00001	I = 08		P = 15		W= 22	10110
C = 02	00010	J = 09		Q = 16		X = 23	
D = 03	00011	K = 10		R= 17		Y = 24	
E = 04	00100	L = 11		S = 18	10010	Z = 25	
F = 05		M = 12		T = 19		= 26	
G = 06		N = 13	01101	U = 20		! = 27	11011

d.   To send the message "NOSE," Arianna's computer would change 13141804 to 0110101110100100100. What would be the computer code for "MATH"?

e.   Decipher Arianna's secret message below. Remember that every 5 digits is a letter.

01111101001100111001010110010011010001011010001101111011

Glossary

5-D Process   An organized method to solve problems. The 5 D's stand for Describe/Draw, Define, Do, Decide, and Declare. This is a problem-solving strategy for which solving begins by making a prediction about the answer or one element of it (a trial), and then confirming whether the result of the trial is correct. If not, information is gained about how close the trial is to the correct value, so that adjustments to the trial value may be made. Being organized is extremely important to the success of this method, as well as writing a usable table. The 5-D Process leads to writing equations to represent word problems. (p. 295)

absolute value   The absolute value of a number is the distance of the number from zero. Since the absolute value represents a distance, without regard to direction, absolute value is always non-negative. Thus, the absolute value of a negative number is its opposite, while the absolute value of a non-negative number is just the number itself. The absolute value of x is usually written "$|x|$." For example, $|-5| = 5$ and $|22| = 22$. (p. 89)

acute angle   An angle with a measure greater than $0°$ and less than $90°$. An example is shown at right. (p. 460)

acute triangle   A triangle with all three angle measures less than $90°$.

addition $(+)$ An operation that tells how many objects there are when two sets are combined. The result is the number of objects in the two sets together which is called a sum. In arithmetic, the word "object" usually means "number."

additive identity   The number 0 is called the additive identity because adding 0 to any number does not change the number. For example, $7 + 0 = 7$. (p. 96)

Additive Identity Property   The Additive Identity Property states that adding zero to any expression leaves the expression unchanged. That is, $a + 0 = a$. For example, $-2 + 0 = -2$.

additive inverse   The number you need to add to a given number to get a sum of 0. For example, the additive inverse of -3 is 3. It is also called the opposite. (p. 96)

Additive Inverse Property   The Additive Inverse Property states that for every number a there is a number $-a$ such that $a = -a = 0$. For example, the number 5 has an additive inverse of -5; $5 + (-5) = 0$. The additive inverse of a number is often called its opposite. For example, 5 and -5 are opposites.

adjacent angles For two angles to be adjacent, they must satisfy these three conditions: (1) The two angles must have a common side; (2) They must have a common vertex; and (3) They can have no interior points in common. This means that the common side must be between the two angles; no overlap between the angles is permitted. In the example at right, $\angle ABC$ and $\angle CBD$ are adjacent angles. (p. 466)

algebra A branch of mathematics that uses variables to generalize the rules of numbers and numerical operations.

algebra tiles An algebra tile is a manipulative whose area represents a constant or variable quantity. The algebra tiles used in this course consist of large squares with dimensions x-by-x; rectangles with dimensions x-by-1; and small squares with dimensions 1-by-1. These tiles are named by their areas: x^2, x, and 1, respectively. The smallest squares are called "unit tiles." In this text, shaded tiles will represent positive quantities while unshaded tiles will represent negative quantities. (p. 220)

algebraic expression See *expression*.

algorithm A fixed rule for carrying out a mathematical procedure. For example, to find the average of a set of values, find the sum of the values and divide by the number of values.

angle Generally, an angle is formed by two rays that are joined at a common endpoint. Angles in geometric figures are usually formed by two segments that have a common endpoint (such as the angle shaded in the figure at right). Also see *acute angle*, *obtuse angle*, and *right angle*. (p. 460)

area For this course, area is the number of square units needed to fill up a region on a flat surface. In later courses, the idea will be extended to cones, spheres, and more complex surfaces. Also see *surface area*. (p. 10)

Area = 15 square units

area model An area model or diagram is one way to represent the probabilities of the outcomes for a sequence of two events. The total area is 1, and the probabilities are represented by proportional parts. In the example, P(S) and P(not S) are the dimensions of the right side of the rectangle. The probabilities that A will occur or not occur are the dimensions of the top of the rectangle. The area of each part is the probability of each possible sequence of two events. (p. 281)

area of a triangle To find the area of a triangle, multiply the length of the base b by the height h and divide by two: $A = \frac{1}{2}bh$. (p. 10)

Associative Property of Addition The Associative Property of Addition states that if a sum contains terms that are grouped, then the sum may be grouped differently with no effect on the total, that is, $a + (b + c) = (a + b) + c$. For example, $3 + (4 + 5) = (3 + 4) + 5$. (p. 190)

Associative Property of Multiplication The Associative Property of Multiplication states that if a product contains terms that are grouped, then the product may be grouped differently with no effect on the result, that is, $a(bc) = (ab)c$. For example, $2 \cdot (3 \cdot 4) = (2 \cdot 3) \cdot 4$. (p. 190)

average The sum of given values divided by the number of values used in computing the sum. For example, the average of $1, 4$, and 10 is $(1 + 4 + 10) / 3$. See *mean*. (p. 13)

axis (plural: axes) On a coordinate plane, two number lines that meet at right angles at the origin $(0, 0)$. The x-axis runs horizontally and the y-axis runs vertically.

bar graph A bar graph is a set of rectangular bars that have height proportional to the number of data elements in each category. Each bar stands for all of the elements in a single distinguishable category (such as "red"). Usually all of the bars are the same width and separated from each other. Also see *histogram*.

base of a geometric figure (a) The base of a triangle: any side of a triangle to which a height is drawn. There are three possible bases in each triangle. (b) The base of a trapezoid: either of the two parallel sides. (c) The base of a parallelogram (including rectangle, rhombus, and square): any side to which a height is drawn. There are four possible bases. (d) The base of a three-dimensional figure. Also see *prism* and *pyramid*.

base of an exponent When working with an exponential expression in the form b^a, b is called the base. For example, 2 is the base in 2^5. (5 is the exponent, and 32 is the value.) See *exponent*.

bin An interval on a histogram.

boundary point The endpoint or endpoints of a ray or segment on a number line where an inequality is true, marked with a solid dot. For strict inequalities (that is, inequalities involving < or >), the point is not part of the solution, and is marked with an open dot. Boundary points may be found by solving the equality associated with the given inequality. For example, the solution to the equation $2x = 6$ is $x = 3$, so the inequality $2x \geq 6$ has a boundary point at 3. A boundary point is also sometimes called a "dividing point." (p. 336)

box plot A graphic way of showing a summary of data using the median, quartiles, and extremes of the data. (p. 404)

center of a circle On a flat surface, the fixed point from which all points on the circle are equidistant. *See* circle.

center of a data distribution Numbers that locate or approximate the center of a data set. Two of the ways to measure the center of a data set are the mean and the median. When dealing with measures of center, it is often useful to consider the distribution of the data. For symmetric distributions with no outliers, the mean can represent the middle, or "typical" value, of the data well. However, in the presence of outliers or non-symmetrical data distributions, the median may be a better measure. *Also see* mean and median. (pp. 13, 19, 393)

certainty When an event will definitely happen. The probability of a certain event is 1.

chord A line segment with its endpoints on a circle. A chord that passes through the center of a circle is called a "diameter." *See* circle. (p. 471)

circle The set of all points on a flat surface that are the same distance from a fixed point. If the fixed point (center) is O, the symbol $\odot O$ represents a circle with center O. If r is the length of a circle's radius and d is the length of its diameter, the circumference of the circle is $C = 2\pi r$ or $C = \pi d$. The area of the circle is $A = \pi r^2$. (p. 471)

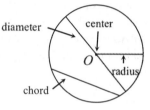

circumference The perimeter (distance around) of a circle. (p. 498)

cluster sample A subgroup of the population that has the similar characteristic of interest as that of the whole population. A cluster sample is one way to obtain a representative sample. (p. 450)

coefficient (numerical) A number multiplying a variable or product of variables. For example, -7 is the coefficient of $-7x$. (p. 331)

combination histogram and box plot A way to visually represent a distribution of data. The box plot is drawn with the same x-axis as the histogram.

combining like terms Combining two or more like terms simplifies an expression by summing constants and summing those variable terms in which the same variables are raised to the same power. For example, combining like terms in the expression $3x + 7 + 5x - 3 + 2x^2 + 3y^2$ gives $8x + 4 + 2x^2 + 3y^2$. When working with algebra tiles, combining like terms involves putting together tiles with the same dimensions. (p. 444)

common Shared.

common factor   A common factor is a factor that is the same for two or more terms. For example, x^2 is a common factor for $3x^2$ and $-5x^2y$.

common multiple   A number that is a multiple of the two or more numbers. For example, 24 and 48 are common multiples of 3 and 8.

Commutative Property of Addition   The Commutative Property of Addition states that if two terms are added, then the order may be reversed with no effect on the total. That is, $a+b=b+a$. For example, $7+12=12+7$. (p. 190)

Commutative Property of Multiplication   The Commutative Property of Multiplication states that if two expressions are multiplied, then the order may be reversed with no effect on the result. That is, $ab=ba$. For example, $5\cdot8=8\cdot5$. (p. 190)

comparison symbol   See *inequality symbol*.

compass   In this course, a compass is tool used to draw circles. (p. 469)

complement   The complement of an event is the set of all outcomes in the sample space that are not included in the event. (p. 265)

complementary angles   Two angles whose measures add up to 90°. Angles T and V are complementary because $m\angle T+m\angle V=90°$. Complementary angles may also be adjacent, like $\angle ABC$ and $\angle CBD$ in the diagram at far right. (p. 466)

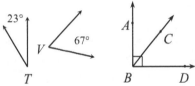

complex fraction   A fraction with a fraction in the numerator and/or denominator.

composite number   A number with more than two factors.

composite shape   A shape made of several simpler shapes. (p. 501)

compound event   A compound event in probability is an outcome that depends on two or more other events. For example, finding the probability that both a red ball and also a blue block are drawn from a bag in two draws. (p. 271, 277)

congruent   Two shapes are congruent if they have exactly the same shape and size. Congruent shapes are similar and have a scale factor of 1.

conjecture   An educated guess that often results from noticing a pattern.

consecutive integers   Integers that are in order without skipping any integers. For example, 8, 9, and 10 are consecutive integers. (p. 302)

constant of proportionality (*k*)   In a proportional relationship, equations are of the form $y = kx$, where *k* is the constant of proportionality. (p. 210)

constant term   A number that is not multiplied by a variable. In the expression $2x + 3(5 - 2x) + 8$, the number 8 is a constant term. The number 3 is not a constant term, because it is multiplied by a variable inside the parentheses. (p. 226, 331)

construction (geometric)   In mathematics, it is the process of using a straightedge and compass to create geometric diagrams. (p. 469)

convenience sample   A subgroup of the population for which it was easy to collect data. A convenience sample is not a random sample. (p. 450)

coordinate   The number corresponding to a point on the number line or an ordered pair (x, y) that corresponds to a point in a two-dimensional coordinate system. In an ordered pair, the *x*-coordinate appears first and the *y*-coordinate appears second. For example, the point $(3, 5)$ has an *x*-coordinate of 3. See *ordered pair*.

coordinate graph (system)   A system of graphing ordered pairs of numbers on a coordinate plane. An ordered pair represents a point, with the first number giving the horizontal position relative to the *x*-axis and the second number giving the vertical position relative to the *y*-axis. Also see *ordered pair*. (p. 87)

corresponding parts   Points, sides, edges, or angles in two or more figures that are images of each other with respect to a transformation. If two figures are congruent, then the corresponding parts of the figures are congruent to each other. See *ratio of similarity* and *congruent*. (p. 194)

counterexample   An example showing that a statement has at least one exception; that is, a situation in which the statement is false. For example, the number 4 is a counterexample to the statement that all even numbers are greater than 7.

cross section   The intersection of a three-dimensional solid and a plane. (p. 509)

cube   A polyhedron of six faces, each of which is a square. (p. 504)

cubic unit   A cube, each of whose edges measure 1 unit in length. Volume is measured in cubic units.

data display   A visual way for organizing information. Data displays used in this course are bar graphs, box plots, dot plots, histograms, scatter plots, stem-and-leaf plots, and Venn diagrams.

decimal point   The dot separating the whole number from the decimal portion, that is, the ones and tenths places in a decimal number.

degree A unit for measuring angles. Usually denoted by ° (the degree symbol). There are 360° in one full rotation. (p. 457)

denominator The lower part of a fraction, which expresses into how many equal parts the whole is divided.

dependent events Two events are dependent if the outcome of one event affects the probability of the other event. For example, if one card is drawn out of a deck of cards, then the probability that the first card is red is $\frac{26}{52} = \frac{1}{2}$ because 26 of the 52 cards are red. However, the probability of the second card now depends on the result of the first selection. If the first card was red, then there are now 25 red cards remaining in a deck of 51 cards, and the probability that the second card is red is $\frac{25}{51}$. The second event (selecting the second card) is dependent on the first event (selecting the first card). (p. 266)

diameter A line segment drawn through the center of a circle with both endpoints on the circle. The length of a diameter is usually denoted d. Note that the length of a circle's diameter is twice the length of its radius. *See* circle. (p. 471)

difference The result of subtraction.

dimensions The dimensions of a figure that is a flat region or space tell how far that the figure extends in each direction. For example, the dimensions of a rectangle might be 16 cm wide by 7 cm high. (p. 511)

Distributive Property For any a, b, and c, $a(b+c) = ab + ac$. For example, $10(7+2) = 10 \cdot 7 + 10 \cdot 2$. (p. 116)

dividend A quantity to be divided. (See *divisor*.)

divisible A number is divisible by another if the remainder of the division is zero.

division (÷) The inverse operation to multiplication, or the operation that creates equal groups.

divisor The quantity by which another quantity is to be divided.
dividend/divisor = quotient + remainder (if there is any).

Dot Plot

dot plot A way of displaying data that has an order and can be placed on a number line. Dot plots are generally used when the data is discrete (separate and distinct) and numerous pieces of data fall on most values.

double-peaked See *shape (of a data display)*.

edge In three dimensions, a line segment formed by the intersection of two faces of a polyhedron. (p. 506)

endpoint   A point that mark the ends of a line segment or ray. (p. 460)

enlarge   To make larger. (p. 399)

enlargement ratio   The ratio of similarity comparing a figure to a similar larger figure is often called the enlargement ratio. This ratio shows by what factor the first figure is enlarged to get the second figure.

equal (=)   Two quantities are equal when they have the same value. For example, when $x = 4$, the expression $x + 8$ is equal to the expression $3x$ because the values of the expressions are the same.

equally likely   Outcomes or events are considered to be equally likely when they have the same probability.

equation   A mathematical sentence in which two expressions have an "equals" sign (=) between them indicating that they have an equal value. For example, the equation $7x + 4.2 = -8$ states that the expression $7x + 4.2$ has the value –8. In this course, an equation is often used to represent a rule relating two quantities.

Equation Mat   An Equation Mat puts two Expression Mats side-by-side to find the value(s) which make the expressions equal. Legal moves are used to find the value(s) that makes the expressions equal. For example, the Equation Mat at right represents the equation $2(x + 1) - 1 = x + 4$. The two sides of the mat are equal when $x = 3$. Also see *"legal" moves*. (p. 339)

equilateral   A polygon is equilateral if all of its sides have equal length. The word "equilateral" comes from "equi" (meaning "equal") and "lateral" (meaning "side"). Equilateral triangles not only have sides of equal length, but also angles of equal measure. However, a polygon with more than three sides may be equilateral without having congruent angles. For example, see the rhombus at right.

equivalent expressions   Two expressions are equivalent if they have the same value. For example, $2 + 3$ is equivalent to $1 + 4$. (p. 88)

equivalent fractions   Two fractions are equivalent if they have the same numerical value. For example, 3/6 and 5/10 are equivalent fractions. (p. 48)

equivalent ratios   Two ratios are equivalent if they have the same value when simplified. (p. 249)

evaluate (an expression) To find the numerical value of. To evaluate an expression, substitute the value(s) given for the variable(s) and perform the operations according to the order of operations. For example, evaluating $2x + y - 10$ when $x = 4$ and $y = 3$ gives the value 1. Also see *expression*. (p. 143)

event One or more results of an experiment. (p. 40)

experimental probability The probability based on data collected in experiments. The experimental probability of an event is defined to be $\frac{\text{number of successful outcomes in the experiment}}{\text{total number of outcomes in the experiment}}$. (p. 40)

exponent In an expression of the form b^a, a is called the exponent. For example, in the expression 2^5, 5 is called the exponent (2 is the base, and 32 is the value). The exponent indicates how many times to use the base as a multiplier. For example, in 2^5, 2 is used 5 times: $2^5 = 2 \cdot 2 \cdot 2 \cdot 2 \cdot 2 = 32$. For exponents of zero, the rule is: for any number $x \neq 0$, $x^0 = 1$. (p. 137)

expression An expression is a combination of individual terms separated by plus or minus signs. Numerical expressions combine numbers and operation symbols; algebraic (variable) expressions include variables. For example, $4 + (5 - 3)$ is a numerical expression. In an algebraic expression, if each of the following terms, $6xy^2$, 24, and $\frac{y-3}{4+x}$, are combined, the result may be $6xy^2 + 24 - \frac{y-3}{4+x}$. An expression does not have an "equals" sign. (p. 137, 331)

Expression Comparison Mat An Expression Comparison Mat puts two Expression Mats side-by-side so they can be compared to see which represents the greater value. For example, in the Expression Comparison Mat at right, Mat A represents –3, while Mat B represents –2. Since $-2 > -3$ Mat B is greater. (p. 319)

Expression Mat An organizing tool used to visually represent an expression with algebra tiles. (p. 230)

face One of the flat surfaces of a polyhedron, including the base(s). (p. 506)

factor (1) In arithmetic: when two or more integers are multiplied, each of the integers is a factor of the product. For example, 4 is a factor of 24, because $4 \cdot 6 = 24$.
(2) In algebra: when two or more algebraic expressions are multiplied together, each of the expressions is a factor of the product. For example, x^2 is a factor of $-17x^2y^3$, because $(x^2)(-17y^3) = -17x^2y^3$. (3) To factor an expression is to write it as a product. For example, the factored form of $3x - 18$ is $3(x - 6)$. (p. 331, 341)

fair game A game in which each player has an equally likely chance of winning. (p. 9)

family of fractions   All fractions that are equivalent to each other form a family of fractions. See *equivalent fractions*. (p. 249)

first quartile (Q1)   The median of the lower half of an ordered set of data is the lower quartile. (p. 387)

formula   An equation that shows a mathematical relationship.

fraction   The quotient of two quantities in the form $\frac{a}{b}$ where b is not equal to 0.

Fraction Busters   "Fraction Busting" is a method of simplifying equations involving fractions that uses the Multiplicative Property of Equality to rearrange the equation so that no fractions remain. To use this method, multiply both sides of an equation by the common denominator of all the fractions in the equation. The result will be an equivalent equation with no fractions. For example, when given the equation $\frac{x}{7}+2=\frac{x}{3}$, we can multiply both sides by the "Fraction Buster" 21. The resulting equation, $3x+42=7x$, is equivalent to the original but contains no fractions. (p. 408)

fraction greater than one   A fraction in which the numerator is greater than the denominator.

frequency   The number of times that something occurs within an interval or data set.

generic rectangle   A type of diagram used to visualize multiplying expressions without algebra tiles. Each expression to be multiplied forms a side length of the rectangle, and the product is the sum of the areas of the sections of the rectangle. For example, the generic rectangle at right may be used to multiply $(2x+5)$ by $(x+3)$. (p. 86, 190)

$$(2x+5)(x+3)=2x^2+11x+15$$

area as a product   area as a sum

Giant One   A fraction that is equal to 1. Multiplying any fraction by a Giant One will create a new fraction equivalent to the original fraction. (p. 48)

graph   A graph represents numerical information in a visual form. The numbers may come from a table, situation (pattern), or rule (equation or inequality). Most of the graphs in this course show points, lines, and/or curves on a two-dimensional coordinate system like the one at right or on a single axis called a number line (see diagram below right).

Core Connections, Course 2

graphic organizer (GO)   A visual representation of concepts or ideas you have learned. It helps with brainstorming and/or organizing information. It can make connections between ideas more clear. Examples are concept maps, charts, and Venn diagrams.

greater than   One expression is greater than another if its value is larger. We indicate this relationship with the greater than symbol ">". For example, $4 + 5$ is greater than $1 + 1$. We write $4 + 5 > 1 + 1$. (p. 322)

greatest common factor (GCF)   For integers, the greatest positive integer that is a common factor of two or more integers. For example, the greatest common factor of 28 and 42 is 14. (p. 322)

height   (a) Triangle: the length of a segment that connects a vertex of the triangle to a line containing the opposite base (side) and is perpendicular to that line. (b) Trapezoid: the length of any segment that connects a point on one base of the trapezoid to the line containing the opposite base and is perpendicular to that line. (c) Parallelogram (includes rectangle, rhombus, and square): the length of any segment that connects a point on one base of the parallelogram to the line containing the opposite base and is perpendicular to that line. (d) Pyramid and cone: the length of the segment that connects the apex to a point in the plane containing the base of a figure and is perpendicular to that plane. (e) Prism or cylinder: the length of a segment that connects one base of the figure to the plane containing the other base and is perpendicular to that plane.

hexagon   A polygon with six sides. (p. 506)

histogram   A way of displaying data that is much like a bar graph in that the height of the bars is proportional to the number of elements. The difference is that each bar of a histogram represents the number of data elements in a range of values, such as the number of people who weigh from 100 pounds up to, but not including, 120 pounds. Each range of values should have the same width. Also see *bar graph*. (p. 382)

horizontal   Parallel to the horizon. The x-axis of a coordinate graph is the horizontal axis. (p. 121)

hundredths grid   A square with an area of 1 unit in which each side is divided into tenths. The area of each small square is $\frac{1}{10}$ by $\frac{1}{10}$ or $\frac{1}{100}$. (p. 154)

Identity Property of Addition   The Identity Property of Addition states that adding zero to any expression leaves the expression unchanged. That is, $a + 0 = a$. For example, $7 + 0 = 7$, and $-2y + 0 = -2y$.

Identity Property of Multiplication   The Identity Property of Multiplication states that multiplying any expression by 1 leaves the expression unchanged. That is, $a(1) = a$. For example, $437x \cdot 1 = 437x$.   (p. 46)

impossibility   An event with a probability of zero.

improper fraction   *See* fraction greater than one.

independent events   If the outcome of a probabilistic event does not affect the probability of another event, then the events are independent. For example, assume that a normal six-sided die is being rolled twice to determine the probability of rolling a 1 twice. The result of the first roll does not affect the probability of rolling a 1 on the second roll. Since the probability of rolling a 1 on the first roll is $\frac{1}{6}$ and the probability of rolling a 1 on the second roll is also $\frac{1}{6}$, then the probability of rolling two 1s in a row is $\frac{1}{6} \cdot \frac{1}{6} = \frac{1}{36}$. (p. 266)

inequality   An inequality consists of two expressions on either side of an inequality symbol. For example, the inequality $7x + 4.2 < -8$ states that the expression $7x + 4.2$ has a value less than –8.   (p. 336)

inequality symbols   The symbol $\leq$ read from left to right means "less than or equal to," the symbol $\geq$ read from left to right means "greater than or equal to," and the symbols $<$ and $>$ mean "less than" and "greater than," respectively. For example, "$7 < 13$" means that 7 is less than 13.   (p. 322)

inference   A statistical prediction.   (p. 455)

integers   The set of numbers $\{\ldots, -3, -2, -1, 0, 1, 2, 3, \ldots\}$.   (p. 91)

interest   An amount paid which is a percentage of an initial value (principal). For example, a savings account may offer 4% annual interest rate, which means they will pay $4.00 in interest for a principal of $100 kept in the account for one year.   (p. 417)

interquartile range (IQR)   A way to measure the spread of data. It is calculated by subtracting the first quartile from the third quartile.   (p. 387)

interval   A set of numbers between two given numbers.   (p. 121)

inverse operation   An operation that undoes another operation. For example, multiplication is the inverse operation for division.

irrational numbers   The set of numbers that cannot be expressed in the form $\frac{a}{b}$, where a and b are integers and $b \neq 0$. For example, π and $\sqrt{2}$ are irrational numbers.   (p. 490)

isosceles trapezoid   A trapezoid with two (non-parallel) sides of equal length.

isosceles triangle   A triangle with two sides of equal length.

lateral face   A (flat) sides of a polyhedron. It is always a polygon. (p. 506)

least common multiple (LCM)   The smallest common multiple of a set of two or more integers. For example, the least common multiple of 4, 6, and 8 is 24.

"legal" moves   When working with an Equation Mat or Expression Comparison Mat, there are certain "legal" moves you can make with the algebra tiles that keep the relationship between the two sides of the mat intact. For example, removing an x tile from the positive region of each side of an equation mat is a legal move; it keeps the expressions on each side of the mat equal. The legal moves are those justified by the properties of the real numbers. (p. 340)

less than   (1) One expression is less than another if its value is not as large. This relationship is indicated with the less than symbol "$<$." For example, $1+1$ is less than $4+5$, so the comparison is written as $1+1 < 4+5$. (2) Sometimes the comparison is made that one amount is a certain quantity less than another amount. For example, a student movie ticket might cost two dollars *less than* an adult ticket. (p. 322)

like terms   Two or more terms that contain the same variable(s), with corresponding variables raised to the same power. For example, $5x^2$ and $2x^2$ are like terms. See *combining like terms*. (p. 226)

line   A line is an undefined term in geometry. A line is one-dimensional and continues without end in two directions. A line is made up of points and has no thickness. A line may be named with a letter (such as l), but also may be labeled using two points on the line, such as $\overleftrightarrow{AB}$ shown the right.

line segment   The portion of a line between two points. A line segment is named using its endpoints. For example, the line segment at right may be named either $\overline{AB}$ or $\overline{BA}$.

lowest common denominator (LCD)   The smallest common multiple of the denominators of two or more fractions. For example, the LCD of $\frac{5}{12}$ and $\frac{3}{8}$ is 24.

lowest terms of a fraction   A fraction for which the numerator and the denominator have no common factor greater than one.

mean   The mean, or average, of several numbers is one way of defining the "middle" of the numbers. To find the average of a group of numbers, add the numbers together then divide by the number of numbers in the set. For example, the average of the numbers 1, 5, and 6 is $(1+5+6) \div 3 = 4$. The mean is generally the best measure of central tendency when there are not outliers in the data set. See *average*. (p. 13)

measure of central tendency   Mean and median are measures of central tendency, reflecting special statistical information about a set of data. See *center (of a data distribution)*. (p. 19)

measurement   For the purposes of this course, a measurement is an indication of the size or magnitude of a geometric figure. For example, an appropriate measurement of a line segment would be its length. Appropriate measurements of a square would include not only the length of a side, but also its area and perimeter. The measure of an angle represents the number of degrees of rotation from one ray to the other about the vertex. (p. 511)

median   The middle number of an ordered set of data. If there is no distinct middle, then the average of the two middle numbers is the median. The median is generally more accurate than the mean as a measure of central tendency when there are outliers in the data set. (p. 19)

mixed number (fraction)   A number that consists of an integer and a fraction. For example, $3\frac{3}{8}$.

multiple   The product of a whole number and any other (nonzero) whole number. For example, 15 is a multiple of 5.

multiple representations of a portion   See *portions web*.

multiplication ($\cdot$)   An operation that reflects repeated addition. For example, $3 \cdot 4 = 4 + 4 + 4$.

multiplicative identity   The number 1 is called the multiplicative identity because multiplying any number by 1 does not change the number. For example, $7(1) = 7$. (p. 48)

Multiplicative Identity Property   The Multiplicative Identity Property states that multiplying any expression by 1 leaves the expression unchanged. That is, $a(1) = a$. For example, $437x \cdot 1 = 437x$. (p. 175)

multiplicative inverse   The multiplicative inverse for a non-zero number is the number we can multiply by to get the multiplicative identity, 1. For example, for the number 5, the multiplicative inverse is $\frac{1}{5}$; for the number $\frac{2}{3}$ the multiplicative inverse is $\frac{3}{2}$. (p. 160)

multiplier   The number you can multiply by in order to increase or decrease an amount. See *scale factor*. (p. 187)

mutually exclusive   Two events are mutually exclusive if they have no outcomes in common. (p. 275)

negative number   A negative number is a number less than zero. Negative numbers are graphed on the negative side of a number line, which is to the left of the origin. (p. 91)

net A drawing of each of the faces of a prism or pyramid, as if it were cut along its edges and flattened out.

number line A diagram representing all real numbers as points on a line. All real numbers are assigned to points. The numbers are called the coordinates of the points and the point for which the number 0 is assigned is called the origin. Also see *boundary point*. (p. 91)

numerator The number above the bar in a fraction that tells the numbers of parts in relationship to the number of parts in the whole.

obtuse angle Any angle that measures between (but not including) 90° and 180°. (p. 460)

obtuse triangle A triangle with one obtuse angle.

octagon A polygon with eight sides. (p. 506)

one-dimensional Something that does not have any width or depth. Lines and curves are one-dimensional. (p. 511)

operation A mathematical process such as addition, subtraction, multiplication, division, raising to a power, or taking a root.

opposite (of a number) The same number but with the opposite sign (+ or −). The additive inverse.

order of operations The specific order in which certain operations are to be carried out to evaluate or simplify expressions: parentheses (or other grouping symbols), exponents (powers or roots), multiplication and division (from left to right), and addition and subtraction (from left to right). (p. 137)

ordered pair Two numbers written in order as follows: (x, y). The primary use of ordered pairs in this course is to represent points in an xy-coordinate system. The first coordinate (x) represents the distance from the x-axis. The second coordinate (y) represents the distance from the y-axis. For example, the ordered pair $(3, 5)$ represents the point shown in bold at right.

origin The point on a coordinate plane where the x-axis and y-axis intersect is called the origin. This point has coordinates $(0, 0)$. The point assigned to zero on a number line is also called the origin. See *axis*.

outcome Possible result in an experiment or consequence of an action. (p. 40, 266)

outlier A number in a set of data that is much larger or much smaller than the other numbers in the set. (p. 393)

parallel Two or more straight lines on a flat surface that do not intersect (no matter how far they are extended) are parallel. The matching arrows on the parallelogram (see below) indicate that those segments are parallel.

parallel box plot A way to visually compare multiple data distributions by drawing each of their box plots on the same axis. (p. 444)

parallelogram A quadrilateral with two pairs of parallel sides. (p. 10)

pentagon A polygon with five sides. (p. 506)

percent (%) A ratio that compares a number to 100. Percents are often written using the "%" symbol. For example, 0.75 is equal to $\frac{75}{100}$ or 75%. (p. 23)

percent ruler A diagram like the one shown at right. It is used to visually aid in determining an amount that is a percent of a whole. (p. 292)

perimeter The distance around a figure on a flat surface. (p. 10)

Perimeter =
$5 + 8 + 4 + 6 = 23$ units

perpendicular Two rays, line segments, or lines that meet (intersect) to form a right angle (90°) are called perpendicular. A line and a flat surface may also be perpendicular if the line does not lie on the flat surface but intersects the surface and forms a right angle with every line on the flat surface passing through the point of intersection. A small square at the point of intersection of two lines or segments indicates that the lines form a right angle and are therefore perpendicular.

pi (π) The ratio of the circumference (C) of the circle to its diameter (d). For every circle, $\pi = \frac{\text{circumference}}{\text{diameter}} = \frac{C}{d}$. Numbers such as 3.14, 3.14159, or $\frac{22}{7}$ are approximations of π. (p. 498)

place value The number assigned to each place that a digit occupies.

plane A plane is a two-dimensional flat surface that extends without end. It is made up of points and has no thickness. (p. 509)

point An exact location in space. In two dimensions, an ordered pair specifies a point on a coordinate plane. See *ordered pair*.

polygon A two-dimensional closed figure of three or more line segments (sides) connected end to end. Each segment is a side and only intersects the endpoints of its two adjacent sides. Each point of intersection is a vertex. At right are two examples of polygons. (p. 506)

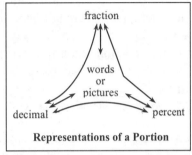

polyhedron A three-dimensional figure with no holes for which all faces are polygons. (p. 506)

population A collection of objects or group of people about whom information is gathered. (p. 450)

portion A part of something; a part of a whole.

portions web The web diagram at right illustrates that fractions, decimals, and percents are different ways to represent a portion of a number. Portions may also be represented in words, such as "four fifths" or "seven fourths," or as diagrams.

Representations of a Portion

positive numbers Numbers that are greater than zero. (p. 91)

power A number or variable raised to an exponent in the form x^n. See *exponent*.

prime factor A factor that is a prime number. (p. 52)

prime factorization The expression of a number as the product of prime factors.

prime number A positive integer with exactly two factors. The only factors of a prime number are 1 and itself. For example, the numbers 2, 3, 17, and 31 are all prime. (p. 52)

principal Initial investment or capital. An initial value. (p. 417)

prism A three-dimensional figure that consists of two parallel congruent polygons (called *bases*) and a vertical surface containing segments connecting each point on each side of one base to the corresponding point on the other base. The lateral surface of a prism consists of parallelograms. (p. 506)

probability A number that represents how likely an event is to happen. When a event has a finite number of equally-likely outcomes, the probability that one of those outcomes, called A, will occur is expressed as a ratio and written as: $P(A) = \frac{\text{number of successful outcomes}}{\text{total number of possible outcomes}}$. For example, when flipping a coin, the probability of getting tails, P(tails), is 1/2 because there is only one tail (successful outcome) out of the two possible equally likely outcomes (a head and a tail). Probability may be written as a ratio, decimal, or percent. A probability of 0 (or 0%) indicates that the occurrence of that outcome is impossible, while a probability of 1 (or 100%) indicates that the event must occur. Events that "might happen" will have values somewhere between 0 and 1 (or between 0% and 100%). (p. 40)

probability table *See area model.*

probability tree Tree diagrams are useful for representing possible outcomes of probability experiments. For example, the tree diagram at right represents the possible outcomes when a coin is flipped twice.

```
      H  HH
   H
      T  HT
      H  TH
   T
      T  TT
```

product The result of multiplying. For example, the product of 4 and 5 is 20.

proportion An equation stating that two ratios (fractions) are equal. For example, the equation at right is a proportion. A proportion is a useful type of equation to set up when solving problems involving proportional relationships. (p. 210)

$$\frac{68 \text{ votes for Mr. Mears}}{100 \text{ people surveyed}} = \frac{34 \text{ votes for Mr. Mears}}{50 \text{ people surveyed}}$$

proportional equation An equation stating that two ratios (fractions) are equal. (p. 210)

proportional relationship Two values are in a proportional relationship if a proportion may be set up that relates the values. (p. 210)

proportions web The web diagram at right illustrates the connections between different representations of the same proportional relationship. (p. 212)

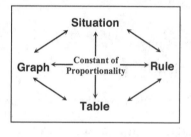

protractor A geometric tool used for physically measuring the number of degrees in an angle. (p. 458)

pyramid A three-dimensional figure with a base that is a polygon. The lateral faces are formed by connecting each vertex of the base to a single point (the vertex of the pyramid) that is above or below the surface that contains the base. (p. 506)

quadrants The coordinate plane is divided by its axes into four quadrants. The quadrants are numbered as shown in the first diagram at right. When graphing data that has no negative values, sometimes a graph that shows only the first quadrant is used.

quadrilateral A polygon with four sides. The shape at right is a quadrilateral. (p. 506)

quartile Along with the median, the quartiles divide a set of data into four groups of the same size. Also see *box plot.* (p. 387)

quotient The result of a division problem. (p. 162)

radius (plural: radii)   A line segment drawn from the center of a circle to a point on the circle. (p. 471)

random   An event is random if its result cannot be known (and can only be guessed) until the event is completed. For example, the flip of a fair coin is random because the coin can either land on heads or tails and the outcome cannot be known for certain until after the coin is flipped.

random number   A number generated by a process whose outcome does not follow any sort of pattern and thus the number cannot be predicted.

random number generator   A computational device designed to generate a set of numbers that lack any pattern. (p. 259)

random sample   A sample which was chosen as a result of a random process. A random sample can represent the whole population well. (p. 455)

range   The range of a set of data is the difference between the highest and lowest values. (p. 387)

rate   A ratio comparing two quantities, often a comparison of time. For example, miles per hour.

ratio   A ratio compares two quantities by division. A ratio may be written using a colon, but is more often written as a fraction. For example, the comparison may be made of the ratio of female students in a particular school to the total number of students in the school. This ratio could be written as 1521:2906 or as the fraction shown at right. (p. 214)

$$\frac{1521 \text{ female students}}{2906 \text{ total students}}$$

ratio of similarity   The ratio of any pair of corresponding sides of two similar figures. This means that once it is determined that two figures are similar, all of the pairs of corresponding sides of the figures have the same ratio. For example, for the similar triangles $\triangle ABC$ and $\triangle DEF$ at right, the ratio of similarity is $\frac{5}{11}$. The ratio of similarity may also be called the linear scale factor. (p. 194)

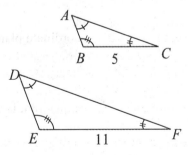

rational numbers   Numbers that may be expressed in the form $\frac{a}{b}$, where a and b are integers and $b \neq 0$. For example, 0.75 is a rational number because 0.75 may be expressed in the form $\frac{3}{4}$. (p. 70)

ray   A ray is part of a line that starts at one point and extends without end in one direction. In the example at right, ray $\overrightarrow{AB}$ is part of $\overleftrightarrow{AB}$ that starts at A and contains all of the points of $\overleftrightarrow{AB}$ that are on the same side of A as point B, including A. Point A is the endpoint of $\overrightarrow{AB}$. (p. 460)

reciprocals   The reciprocal of a nonzero number is its multiplicative inverse, that is, the reciprocal of x is $\frac{1}{x}$. For a number in the form $\frac{a}{b}$, where a and b are non-zero, the reciprocal is $\frac{b}{a}$. The product of a number and its reciprocal is 1. For example, the reciprocal of 12 is $\frac{1}{12}$, because $12 \cdot \frac{1}{12} = 1$. (p. 160)

rectangle   A quadrilateral with four right angles. (p. 10)

reduce   To make smaller. (p. 399)

regular polygon   A polygon is regular if the polygon is a convex polygon with congruent angles and congruent sides. For example, the shape at right is a regular hexagon.

REGULAR HEXAGON

repeating decimal   A repeating decimal is a decimal that repeats the same sequence of digits forever from some point onward. For example, 4.56073073073... is a decimal for which the three digits 073 continue to repeat forever. Repeating decimals are always the decimal expansions of rational numbers. (p. 81)

representative sample   A subgroup of the population that has the similar characteristic of interest as that of the whole population. Representative samples are usually the result of random sampling. (p. 450)

remainder   The amount left over when the divisor does not divide the dividend exactly. For example $63 \div 5$ is 12 with a remainder of 3.

rewrite   To rewrite an equation or expression is to write an equivalent equation or expression. Rewriting could involve using the Distributive Property, combining like terms, or using Fraction Busters. We usually rewrite in order to change expressions or equations into more useful forms or sometimes, just simpler forms. (p. 146)

rhombus   A quadrilateral with four congruent sides. Also see *equilateral*.

right angle   An angle that measures 90°. A small square is used to note a right angle, as shown in the example at right.

90°

right triangle   A triangle that has one right angle. The side of a right triangle opposite the right angle is called the "hypotenuse," and the two sides adjacent to the right angle are called "legs."

hypotenuse

leg #2

leg #1

round (a number)   To express an approximate value of a number that is exact to a given decimal place. For example, if the number 1234.56 is 1235 when rounded to the nearest whole number and is 1200 when rounded to the nearest 100.

rule   A rule is an equation or inequality that represents the relationship between two numerical quantities. A rule is often used to represent the relationship between quantities in a table, a pattern, a real-world situation, or a graph.

sample   A subset (group) of a given population with the same characteristics as the whole population. (p. 450)

sample space   The collection of all possible outcomes of an event. (p. 400)

scale (scaling)   The ratio between a length of the representation (such as a map, model, or diagram) and the corresponding length of the actual object. For example, the map of a city may use one inch to represent one mile. (p. 36)

scale drawing   A drawing that shows a real object with accurate sizes except they have all been reduced or enlarged by a certain amount (called the scale factor). (p. 192)

scale factor   A ratio that compares the sizes of the parts of one figure or object to the sizes of the corresponding parts of a similar figure or object. In this course it is also referred to as the multiplier. (p. 194)

scale on axes   The scale on an axis tells you what number each successive tick mark on the axis represents. A complete graph has the scale marked with numbers on each axis. Each axis should be scaled so that each interval represents the same amount. (p. 121)

scalene triangle   A triangle with no congruent sides. (p. 293)

scatter plot   Two related sets of data may have the corresponding values of the sets listed as ordered pairs. If these ordered pairs are graphed in the coordinate plane, then the result is a scatter plot.

set   A collection of items.

shape (of a data display)   Statisticians use the following words to describe the overall shape of a data distribution: symmetric, skewed, single-peaked, double-peaked, and uniform. Examples are shown below. (p. 393)

side of an angle   One of the two rays that form an angle.

similar figures   Similar figures have the same shape but are not necessarily the same size. For example the two triangles at right are similar. In similar figures, the measures of corresponding angles are equal and the ratio of the corresponding sides lengths are equal. (p. 194)

simple interest   Interest paid on the principal alone. (p. 417)

simplify   To simplify an expression is to write a less complicated expression with the same value. A simplified expression has no parentheses and no like terms. For example, the expression $3 - (2x + 7) - 4x$ may be simplified to $-4 - 6x$. When working with algebra tiles, a simplified expression uses the fewest possible tiles to represent the original expression. (p. 226)

simulation (probability)   When conducting an experiment with an event that is unrealistic to perform, a simulation can be used. A simulation is a similar experiment that has the same probabilities as the original experiment. (p. 259)

single-peaked   See *shape (of a data display)*. (p. 393)

skewed (data display)   See *shape (of a data display)*. (p. 393)

solution   The number or numbers that when substituted into an equation or inequality make the equation or inequality true. For example, $x = 4$ is a solution to the equation $3x = 12$ because $3x$ equals 12 when $x = 4$. (p. 363)

solve   To find all the solutions to an equation or an inequality. The solution(s) may be number(s), variable(s), or an expression. (p. 340)

spread (data display)   A measure of the amount of variability in a data set. Three ways to measure spread are the range, the mean absolute deviation, and the interquartile range. (p. 387)

square   A quadrilateral with four right angles and four congruent sides.

square

square units   The units used to describe the measure of an area in the form of 1×1 unit squares.

stem-and-leaf plot   A frequency distribution that arranges data so that all digits except the last digit in each piece of data are in the stem, the last digit of each piece of data are the leaves, and both stems and leaves are arranged in order from least to greatest. The example at right displays the data: 49, 52, 54, 58, 61, 61, 67, 68, 72, 73, 73, 73, 78, 82, 83, 108, 112, and 117. (p. 382)

"leaf"

4	9
5	2 4 8
6	1 1 7 8
7	2 3 3 3 8
8	2 3
9	
10	8
11	2 7

"stem"

Core Connections, Course 2

stoplight icon   The icon (shown at right) will appear periodically throughout the text. Problems that display this icon contain errors of some type. (p. 43)

straight angle   An angle that measures 180°. This occurs when the rays of the angle point in opposite directions, forming a line. (p. 460)

straightedge   A tool used as a guide to draw lines, rays, and segments. (p. 469)

subproblems   A problem solving strategy that breaks a problem into smaller parts that must be solved in order to solve the original, more complex problem.

substitution   Replacing one symbol with a number, a variable, or another algebraic expression of the same value. Substitution does not change the value of the overall expression. For example, suppose that the expression $13x - 6$ must be evaluated for $x = 4$. Since x has the value 4, 4 may be substituted into the expression wherever x appears, giving the equivalent expression $13(4) - 6$. (p. 143)

subtraction (−)   An operation that gives the difference between two numbers. (p. 147)

sum   The result of adding two or more numbers. For example, the sum of 4 and 5 is 9.

Super Giant One   A Giant One in which either or both the numerator and denominator are fractions. (p. 165)

supplementary angles   Two angles a and b for which $a + b = 180°$. Each angle is called the supplement of the other. In the example at right, angles A and B are supplementary. Supplementary angles are often adjacent. For example, since $\angle LMN$ is a straight angle, then $\angle LMP$ and $\angle PMN$ are supplementary angles because $m\angle LMP + m\angle PMN = 180°$. (p. 466)

surface area   The sum of all the area(s) of the surface(s) of a three-dimensional solid. For example, the surface area of a prism is the sum of the areas of its top and bottom bases, and its vertical surfaces (lateral faces). (p. 503)

symmetric   See *shape (of a data display)*. (p. 393)

systematic list   A list created by following a system (organized process). When finding probabilities, a systematic list helps to find all outcomes of a sample space or event. (p. 277)

term A term is a single number, variable, or the product of numbers and variables, such as -45, $1.2x$, and $3xy^2$. (p. 137)

terminating decimal A terminating decimal is a decimal that has only a finite number of non-zero digits, such as 4.067. Terminating decimals are a particular kind of repeating decimal for which the repeating portion is zeros, so the example could be written 4.0670000000... but it is not necessary to write the zeros at the end. (p. 81)

theoretical probability A calculated probability based on the possible outcomes when each outcome has the same chance of occurring: (number of successful outcomes)/(total number of possible outcomes). (p. 40)

third quartile (Q3) The median of the upper half of an ordered set of data. (p. 387)

three-dimensional An object that has height, width, and depth. (p. 511)

tick mark A symbol that shows that a number line has been divided into intervals of equal length. See *number line*.

trapezoid A quadrilateral with at least one pair of parallel sides. (p. 10)

triangle A polygon with three sides. (p. 506)

triangle inequality In a triangle with side lengths a, b, and c, c must be less than the sum of a and b and greater than the difference of a and b. In the example at right, a is greater than b (that is, $a > b$), so the possible values for c are all numbers such that $c > a - b$ and $c < a + b$. (p. 476)

two-dimensional An object having length and width. (p. 511)

uniform See *shape (of a data display)*. (p. 393)

unit of measure A standard quantity (such as a centimeter, second, square foot, or gallon) that is used to measure and describe an object. A single object may be measured using different units of measure. For example, a pencil may be 80 mm long, meaning that the pencil is 80 times as long as a unit of 1 mm. However, the same pencil is 8 cm long, so that the pencil is the same length as 8 cm laid end-to-end. This is because 1 cm is the same length as 10 mm.

unit rate A rate with a denominator of one when simplified. (p. 214)

variability *See* spread.

variable A symbol used to represent one or more numbers. In this course, letters of the English alphabet are used as variables. For example, in the expression $3x - (8.6xy + z)$, the variables are x, y, and z. (p. 220)

variable expression See *expression*.

vertex (plural: vertices) (1) For a two-dimensional geometric shape, a vertex is a point where two or more line segments or rays meet to form a "corner," such as in a polygon or angle. (2) For a three-dimensional polyhedron, a vertex is a point where the edges of the solid meet. (p. 460, 506)

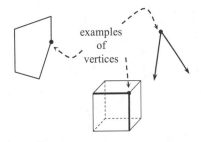

examples of vertices

vertical At right angles to the horizon. On a coordinate graph, the y-axis runs vertically. (p. 121)

vertical angles The two opposite (that is, non-adjacent) angles formed by two intersecting lines. "Vertical" is a relationship between pairs of angles, so one angle cannot be called vertical. Angles that form a vertical pair are always congruent. (p. 466)

volume A measurement of the size of the three-dimensional region enclosed within an object. Volume is expressed as the number of $1 \times 1 \times 1$ unit cubes (or parts of cubes) that fit inside a solid. (p. 511)

voluntary response sample A subgroup of the population that chose to respond to a survey. A voluntary response sample is not a random sample. (p. 450)

x-axis The horizontal number line on a coordinate graph. See *axis*.

x-coordinate In an ordered pair, (x, y), that represents a point in the coordinate plane, x is the value of the x-coordinate. That is, the distance from the y-axis that is needed to plot the point. (p. 87)

y-axis The vertical number line on a coordinate graph. See *axis*.

y-coordinate In an ordered pair, (x, y), that represents a point in the coordinate plane, y is the value of the y-coordinate. That is, the distance from the x-axis that is needed to plot the point. (p. 87)

zero pair Two quantities whose sum is zero. A number and its opposite make a zero pair because their sum is 0. (p. 231)

Index
Student Version

Many of the pages referenced here contain a definition or an example of the topic listed, often within the body of a Math Notes box. Others contain problems that develop or demonstrate the topic. It may be necessary to read the text on several pages to fully understand the topic. Also, some problems listed here are good examples of the topic and may not offer any explanation. The page numbers below reflect the pages in the Student Version. References to Math Notes boxes are bolded.

5-D Process, 291, **295**, 298, 304, 352
   strategies for using, 293

A
Absolute value, 89
Acute angle, **460**, 462
Addition
   Associative Property of, 171, **190**
   Commutative Property of, 171, **190**
   connecting with subtraction, 145, 146, 151
   of fractions, 50, 51
   of integers, 88, 93, 95, **96**, **101**, 159
   of rational numbers, 88, 93
   repeated, 98
   using a number line, 89
Additive identity, **96**
Additive inverse, **96**, **151**
Adjacent angles, 464, **466**
Algebra tiles, **220**
   area, 217
   legend, 319
   naming, **220**
   perimeter, 218, **226**
   removing balanced sets, 320
   removing zeros, 320
Algebraic expression, **143**, 216, 217, **220**
   evaluating, **143**
Angle, 457, **460**, 462, **466**
   acute, **460**, 462
   adjacent, 464, **466**
   classifying, 462
   complementary, 463, **466**
   degree of, 457
   measurement of, 458, **460**, 462
   naming, **466**
   obtuse, **460**, 462
   right, **460**, 462
   straight, **460**, 462
   supplementary, 463, **466**

   vertex, **460**, 462
   vertical, 464, **466**
Angle ruler. *See* protractor
Area, **10**, **511**
   algebra tiles, 217
   Checkpoint 1, 61, 538
   of a circle, 495, 496, 497, **498**
   of a parallelogram, **10**
   of a rectangle, **10**
   of a trapezoid, **10**
   of a triangle, **10**
   of composite shapes, 501
Area model
   for probability, 281
Arguments
   construct viable, 527
Arithmetic average, **13**
Arithmetic properties, 171
Associative Property of Addition, 171, **190**
Associative Property of Multiplication, 173, **190**
Average, 14, *Also see* mean
Axis
   scaling, **36**, **121**

B
Balanced set
   removing, 320, **340**
Base
   prism, 504, **506**
Becoming Mathematically Proficient, 527, 531, 535
Birthday Sweets, 513
Boundary point, 333, 334, **336**
   finding, 335
   open circle, **336**

Polygon, **506**
Polyhedron, **506**
  edge, **506**
  face, **506**
Polynomioes! (PI-5), 563
Population, 447, **450**
  random sample, **455**
Portion. *See* fraction
Portions web, 23, **24**, 45, 77, **81**
Positive numbers
  number line, **91**
Positive tiles, 139
Possible outcome, 27, **40**
Prime
  factor, 52
  number, 52
Principal, 415, **417**
Prism, **506**
  base, 504, **506**
  face, 504
  pentagonal, **506**
  rectangular, 503, 512
  right rectangular, 504
  surface area, 504
  triangular, **506**
  volume, 504, 510, 513, 517, **519**
Probability, 2, 26, 27, **40**
  and, 54, 263, 273, 275, **277**
  area model, 281
  complement, 255
  compound, 54, 263, **271**, 273, **277**, 280
  dependent event, 264, **266**
  desired outcome, 27
  either/or, 54, 55, 57, 255, 263, **271**
  event, 38, **40**, **266**
  experimental, 29, **40**
  games, 255
  independent event, 263, 264, **266**
  multiple events, 263, 273, **277**
  outcome, **40**, **266**
  possible outcome, 27
  sample space, 38, **40**
  simulation, 259
  subtracting to find, 57
  systematic list, **277**
  table, 280
  tables, 268, 269
  theoretical, 27, 35, **40**
  tree diagram, 273, 274, **277**
  using to make predictions, 32

Product. *Also see* multiplication
  positive or negative?, 157
Properties
  mathematical, **190**
Properties of addition
  Associative, 171, **190**
  Commutative, 171, **190**
Properties of multiplication
  Associative, 173, **190**
  Commutative, 173, **190**
Proportion
  solving, 423, **426**
    Checkpoint 9, 520, 557
Proportional relationship, 15, 196, 199, 200,
  207, **210**, 381
  connections web, 212, 213
  constant of proportionality, **210**, 212
  distance, rate, and time, 379, 380, 381
  equation, 207, **210**
  finding missing information in, 420
  graphing, 202, 207, **210**
  in a table, 202, 209, **210**
  ratio of circumference to diameter, 489,
    490
Protractor, 458, 462, 463
Puzzle Investigator problems, 559
Pyramid, **506**, 511
  rectangular, 510

Q

Quadrilateral, **506**
Quantities
  describing relationships between, 286
  representing, 298
  scaling, 384, 390, **399**
Quartile, **387**
  box plot, **404**
  Checkpoint 7B, 428, 551
  first, **387**, **404**
  third, **387**, **404**
Quotient, 162, 164, *Also see* division

R

Radius, **471**, 496
Random Number Generator, 259
Random sample, 453, **455**
Range, **387**, 438

Rate
  interest, 415, **417**
  of change, **214**
  relationship to distance and time, 379,
    380, 381
  unit, 207, **214**
Ratio, 246, **249**
  application, 533
  equivalent, **249**
  percent, **253**
  rate of change, **214**
Rational numbers, 70, 162
  adding, 88, 93
  division, 162
Ray, **460**, 462, **466**
Reasoning
  critiquing that of others, 527
  repeated, 531
Reciprocal, **160**
  fraction division, **165**
Recorder/Reporter, 4
Rectangle
  area, **10**
Rectangular prism, 512
Reduce, 187, **399**
Removing
  balanced sets, 320, **340**
  zeros, 320, 324, **340**
Renting the Hall, 415
Repeated reasoning, 531
Repeating decimal, 22, 71, 73, 78
  as a fraction, 79, **81**
Representations of a portion
  Checkpoint 2, 118, 541
Representations of a Portion web, 23, **24**, 45,
  81
Representative sample, 447, **450**, **455**
Resource Manager, 4
Response sample, voluntary, 448, **450**
Rewriting an expression, 146
Right angle, **460**, 462
Rock-Paper-Scissors, 264, 265
Rotation, 457
Ruler
  to measure angles. *See* protractor

S
Sample, 447, **450**, *Also see* survey
  cluster, 448, **450**
  convenience, 448, **450**
  population, **450**
  random, 453, **455**
  representative, 447, **450**, **455**
  voluntary response, **450**
Sample space, 38, **40**
  complement, 255
  modifying, 38
Sampling techniques, 448, 493
Scale, 192, **399**
  graphing, 113, 114, 119, **121**
  interval, **121**
  on a map, 193
Scale drawing, 192, 193, 530
Scale factor, 187, **194**, 384, 385, 390, 391,
  397, **399**, 410, *Also see* multiplier
Scalene triangle, 293
Scaling, **36**, 384, 385, 390
  interval, **36**
  volume, 526
Scavenger Hunt, 316
Secret Code (PI-14), 570
Septagon, **506**
Shape
  of a data distribution, **393**
Shape Challenge, 236, 237
Shapes
  similar, 187, 189, 192, **194**, 384
Shell Box, The, 517
Similar, 192
Similar figures, 187, 189, **194**, 384
Simple interest, 415, **417**
Simplify, **226**
  an expression, 132, 146
    term, 132, 135
      Checkpoint 7A, 400, 549
      Order of Operations, **137**
  legal move, 320, 327
  removing zeros, 320, 324
  with zero, 229
Simulation
  probability, 259
Single-peaked
  data distribution, **393**
Skewed
  data distribution, **393**

Unit rate, 207, **214**
  Checkpoint 9, 520, 557

V

Variability. *See* spread
Variable, 216, **220**, **331**
  consecutive integer, **302**
  defining, **355**
Variable expression, **143**, *Also see* Algebraic
  expression
Vertex, **466**
  of an angle, **460**, 462
  of a polygon, **506**
Vertical angles, 464, **466**
Vertical axis
  scale, 114, **121**
Volume, 503, **511**
  as related to cross sections, 510
  prism, 504, 510, 513, 517, **519**
  scale factor, 526
Voluntary response sample, 448, **450**

W

Way to Go! (PI-10), 567
Win-A-Row, 94
With of Without Frosting (PI-11), 568
Word problem
  solving, 290
    5-D Process, **295**, 298, 304
  writing equation, 352

X

x-value
  coordinate, 87

Y

Yougurt Shop, The, 208
y-value
  coordinate, 87

Z

Zero, 229
  additive identity, **96**
  additive inverse, **96**
  division by, 232
  making, 90, 91, **101**
  removing, 320, 324, **340**
Zero pair, 231, 319

Common Core State Standards for Mathematics

Mathematics | Grade 7

In Grade 7, instructional time should focus on four critical areas: (1) developing understanding of and applying proportional relationships; (2) developing understanding of operations with rational numbers and working with expressions and linear equations; (3) solving problems involving scale drawings and informal geometric constructions, and working with two- and three-dimensional shapes to solve problems involving area, surface area, and volume; and (4) drawing inferences about populations based on samples.

(1) Students extend their understanding of ratios and develop understanding of proportionality to solve single- and multi-step problems. Students use their understanding of ratios and proportionality to solve a wide variety of percent problems, including those involving discounts, interest, taxes, tips, and percent increase or decrease. Students solve problems about scale drawings by relating corresponding lengths between the objects or by using the fact that relationships of lengths within an object are preserved in similar objects. Students graph proportional relationships and understand the unit rate informally as a measure of the steepness of the related line, called the slope. They distinguish proportional relationships from other relationships.

(2) Students develop a unified understanding of number, recognizing fractions, decimals (that have a finite or a repeating decimal representation), and percents as different representations of rational numbers. Students extend addition, subtraction, multiplication, and division to all rational numbers, maintaining the properties of operations and the relationships between addition and subtraction, and multiplication and division. By applying these properties, and by viewing negative numbers in terms of everyday contexts (e.g., amounts owed or temperatures below zero), students explain and interpret the rules for adding, subtracting, multiplying, and dividing with negative numbers. They use the arithmetic of rational numbers as they formulate expressions and equations in one variable and use these equations to solve problems.

(3) Students continue their work with area from Grade 6, solving problems involving the area and circumference of a circle and surface area of three-dimensional objects. In preparation for work on congruence and similarity in Grade 8 they reason about relationships among two-dimensional figures using scale drawings and informal geometric constructions, and they gain familiarity with the relationships between angles formed by intersecting lines. Students work with three-dimensional figures, relating them to two-dimensional figures by examining cross-sections. They solve real-world and mathematical problems involving area, surface area, and volume of two- and three-dimensional objects composed of triangles, quadrilaterals, polygons, cubes, and right prisms.

(4) Students build on their previous work with single data distributions to compare two data distributions and address questions about differences between populations. They begin informal work with random sampling to generate data sets and learn about the importance of representative samples for drawing inferences.

7 Grade 7 Overview

Ratios and Proportional Relationships

- Analyze proportional relationships and use them to solve real-world and mathematical problems.

The Number System

- Apply and extend previous understandings of operations with fractions to add, subtract, multiply, and divide rational numbers.

- Know that there are numbers that are not rational and approximate them by rational numbers.

Expressions and Equations

- Use properties of operations to generate equivalent expressions.

- Solve real-life and mathematical problems using numerical and algebraic expressions and equations.

Geometry

- Draw, construct and describe geometrical figures and describe the relationships between them.

- Solve real-life and mathematical problems involving angle measure, area, surface area, and volume.

- Solve real-life and mathematical problems involving volume of cylinders, cones, and spheres.

Statistics and Probability

- Use random sampling to draw inferences about a population.

- Draw informal comparative inferences about two populations.

- Investigate chance processes and develop, use, and evaluate probability models.

Mathematical Practices

1. Make sense of problems and persevere in solving them.

2. Reason abstractly and quantitatively.

3. Construct viable arguments and critique the reasoning of others.

4. Model with mathematics.

5. Use appropriate tools strategically.

6. Attend to precision.

7. Look for and make use of structure.

8. Look for and express regularity in repeated reasoning.

Ratios and Proportional Relationships   7.RP

Analyze proportional relationships and use them to solve real-world and mathematical problems.

1. Compute unit rates associated with ratios of fractions, including ratios of lengths, areas and other quantities measured in like or different units. *For example, if a person walks 1/2 mile in each 1/4 hour, compute the unit rate as the complex fraction $^{1/2}/_{1/4}$ miles per hour, equivalently 2 miles per hour.*

2. Recognize and represent proportional relationships between quantities.
   a. Decide whether two quantities are in a proportional relationship, e.g., by testing for equivalent ratios in a table or graphing on a coordinate plane and observing whether the graph is a straight line through the origin.
   b. Identify the constant of proportionality (unit rate) in tables, graphs, equations, diagrams, and verbal descriptions of proportional relationships.
   c. Represent proportional relationships by equations. *For example, if total cost t is proportional to the number n of items purchased at a constant price p, the relationship between the total cost and the number of items can be expressed as t = pn.*
   d. Explain what a point *(x, y)* on the graph of a proportional relationship means in terms of the situation, with special attention to the points (0, 0) and (1, *r*) where *r* is the unit rate.

3. Use proportional relationships to solve multistep ratio and percent problems. *Examples: simple interest, tax, markups and markdowns, gratuities and commissions, fees, percent increase and decrease, percent error.*

The Number System   7.NS

Apply and extend previous understandings of operations with fractions to add, subtract, multiply, and divide rational numbers.

1. Apply and extend previous understandings of addition and subtraction to add and subtract rational numbers; represent addition and subtraction on a horizontal or vertical number line diagram.
   a. Describe situations in which opposite quantities combine to make 0. *For example, a hydrogen atom has 0 charge because its two constituents are oppositely charged.*
   b. Understand $p + q$ as the number located a distance $|q|$ from p, in the positive or negative direction depending on whether q is positive or negative. Show that a number and its opposite have a sum of 0 (are additive inverses). Interpret sums of rational numbers by describing real-world contexts.
   c. Understand subtraction of rational numbers as adding the additive inverse, $p - q = p + (-q)$. Show that the distance between two rational numbers on the number line is the absolute value of their difference, and apply this principle in real-world contexts.
   d. Apply properties of operations as strategies to add and subtract rational numbers.

2. Apply and extend previous understandings of multiplication and division and of fractions to multiply and divide rational numbers.
   a. Understand that multiplication is extended from fractions to rational numbers by requiring that operations continue to satisfy the properties of operations, particularly the distributive property, leading to products such as $(-1)(-1) = 1$ and the rules for multiplying signed numbers. Interpret products of rational numbers by describing real-world contexts.
   b. Understand that integers can be divided, provided that the divisor is not zero, and every quotient of integers (with non-zero divisor) is a rational number. If p and q are integers, then $-(p/q) = (-p)/q = p/(-q)$. Interpret quotients of rational numbers by describing real world contexts.

Grade 7

c. Apply properties of operations as strategies to multiply and divide rational numbers.

d. Convert a rational number to a decimal using long division; know that the decimal form of a rational number terminates in 0s or eventually repeats.

3. Solve real-world and mathematical problems involving the four operations with rational numbers.[1]

Expressions and Equations   7.EE

Use properties of operations to generate equivalent expressions.

1. Apply properties of operations as strategies to add, subtract, factor, and expand linear expressions with rational coefficients.

2. Understand that rewriting an expression in different forms in a problem context can shed light on the problem and how the quantities in it are related. *For example, a + 0.05a = 1.05a means that "increase by 5%" is the same as "multiply by 1.05."*

Solve real-life and mathematical problems using numerical and algebraic expressions and equations.

3. Solve multi-step real-life and mathematical problems posed with positive and negative rational numbers in any form (whole numbers, fractions, and decimals), using tools strategically. Apply properties of operations to calculate with numbers in any form; convert between forms as appropriate; and assess the reasonableness of answers using mental computation and estimation strategies. *For example: If a woman making $25 an hour gets a 10% raise, she will make an additional 1/10 of her salary an hour, or $2.50, for a new salary of $27.50. If you want to place a towel bar 9 3/4 inches long in the center of a door that is 27 1/2 inches wide, you will need to place the bar about 9 inches from each edge; this estimate can be used as a check on the exact computation.*

4. Use variables to represent quantities in a real-world or mathematical problem, and construct simple equations and inequalities to solve problems by reasoning about the quantities.

    a. Solve word problems leading to equations of the form $px + q = r$ and $p(x + q) = r$, where p, q, and r are specific rational numbers. Solve equations of these forms fluently. Compare an algebraic solution to an arithmetic solution, identifying the sequence of the operations used in each approach. *For example, the perimeter of a rectangle is 54 cm. Its length is 6 cm. What is its width?*

    b. Solve word problems leading to inequalities of the form $px + q > r$ or $px + q < r$, where p, q, and r are specific rational numbers. Graph the solution set of the inequality and interpret it in the context of the problem. *For example: As a salesperson, you are paid $50 per week plus $3 per sale. This week you want your pay to be at least $100. Write an inequality for the number of sales you need to make, and describe the solutions.*

Geometry   7.G

Draw, construct, and describe geometrical figures and describe the relationships between them.

1. Solve problems involving scale drawings of geometric figures, including computing actual lengths and areas from a scale drawing and reproducing a scale drawing at a different scale.

2. Draw (freehand, with ruler and protractor, and with technology) geometric shapes with given conditions. Focus on constructing triangles from three measures of angles or sides, noticing when the conditions determine a unique triangle, more than one triangle, or no triangle.

3. Describe the two-dimensional figures that result from slicing three-dimensional figures, as in plane sections of right rectangular prisms and right rectangular pyramids.

---

[1] Computations with rational numbers extend the rules for manipulating fractions to complex fractions.

Core Connections, Course 2

Solve real-life and mathematical problems involving angle measure, area, surface area, and volume.

4. Know the formulas for the area and circumference of a circle and use them to solve problems; give an informal derivation of the relationship between the circumference and area of a circle.
5. Use facts about supplementary, complementary, vertical, and adjacent angles in a multi-step problem to write and solve simple equations for an unknown angle in a figure.
6. Solve real-world and mathematical problems involving area, volume and surface area of two- and three-dimensional objects composed of triangles, quadrilaterals, polygons, cubes, and right prisms.

Statistics and Probability   7.SP

Use random sampling to draw inferences about a population.

1. Understand that statistics can be used to gain information about a population by examining a sample of the population; generalizations about a population from a sample are valid only if the sample is representative of that population. Understand that random sampling tends to produce representative samples and support valid inferences.
2. Use data from a random sample to draw inferences about a population with an unknown characteristic of interest. Generate multiple samples (or simulated samples) of the same size to gauge the variation in estimates or predictions. *For example, estimate the mean word length in a book by randomly sampling words from the book; predict the winner of a school election based on randomly sampled survey data. Gauge how far off the estimate or prediction might be.*

Draw informal comparative inferences about two populations.

3. Informally assess the degree of visual overlap of two numerical data distributions with similar variabilities, measuring the difference between the centers by expressing it as a multiple of a measure of variability. *For example, the mean height of players on the basketball team is 10 cm greater than the mean height of players on the soccer team, about twice the variability (mean absolute deviation) on either team; on a dot plot, the separation between the two distributions of heights is noticeable.*
4. Use measures of center and measures of variability for numerical data from random samples to draw informal comparative inferences about two populations. *For example, decide whether the words in a chapter of a seventh-grade science book are generally longer than the words in a chapter of a fourth-grade science book.*

Investigate chance processes and develop, use, and evaluate probability models.

5. Understand that the probability of a chance event is a number between 0 and 1 that expresses the likelihood of the event occurring. Larger numbers indicate greater likelihood. A probability near 0 indicates an unlikely event, a probability around 1/2 indicates an event that is neither unlikely nor likely, and a probability near 1 indicates a likely event.
6. Approximate the probability of a chance event by collecting data on the chance process that produces it and observing its long-run relative frequency, and predict the approximate relative frequency given the probability. *For example, when rolling a number cube 600 times, predict that a 3 or 6 would be rolled roughly 200 times, but probably not exactly 200 times.*
7. Develop a probability model and use it to find probabilities of events. Compare probabilities from a model to observed frequencies; if the agreement is not good, explain possible sources of the discrepancy.

Grade 7

    a.   Develop a uniform probability model by assigning equal probability to all outcomes, and use the model to determine probabilities of events. *For example, if a student is selected at random from a class, find the probability that Jane will be selected and the probability that a girl will be selected.*

    b.   Develop a probability model (which may not be uniform) by observing frequencies in data generated from a chance process. *For example, find the approximate probability that a spinning penny will land heads up or that a tossed paper cup will land open-end down. Do the outcomes for the spinning penny appear to be equally likely based on the observed frequencies?*

8.   Find probabilities of compound events using organized lists, tables, tree diagrams, and simulation.

    a.   Understand that, just as with simple events, the probability of a compound event is the fraction of outcomes in the sample space for which the compound event occurs.

    b.   Represent sample spaces for compound events using methods such as organized lists, tables and tree diagrams. For an event described in everyday language (e.g., "rolling double sixes"), identify the outcomes in the sample space which compose the event.

    c.   Design and use a simulation to generate frequencies for compound events. *For example, use random digits as a simulation tool to approximate the answer to the question: If 40% of donors have type A blood, what is the probability that it will take at least 4 donors to find one with type A blood?*

THIS BOOK IS THE
PROPERTY OF:

Book No._____

ISSUED TO	Year Used	CONDITION	
		ISSUED	RETURNED

PUPILS to whom this texbook is issued must not write on any part of it in any way, unless otherwise instructed by the teacher.